A PANDEMIC NURSE'S DIARY

By Nurse T

With Timothy Sheard

A Pandemic Nurse's Diary, by Nurse T, with Timothy Sheard, Copyright © 2020 by Timothy Sheard.

All rights reserved.

No part of this book may be reproduced or transmitted in any form or by an electronic or mechanical means, including photocopying, recording or by any information storage and retrieval system, without the express written permission of the publisher, except where permitted by law ("fair use"). Published by Hard Ball Press.

ISBN: 978-1-7344938-4-9

Exterior and interior book design by D. Bass.

Illustrations by Anna Usacheva

Information available at: www.hardballpress.com

Library of Congress Cataloging-in-Publication Data
March, Richard

A Pandemic Nurse's Diary — Nonfiction. 1. Nurse. 2. Pandemic. 3. Hospital care. 4. New York City pandemic. 5. Public health.

Dedication

We dedicate these stories and meditations to the hospital, nursing home and emergency medical service workers who risked their lives in order to care for the frightened patients suffering from Covid-19, to their families and friends, and to the patients and their loved ones. We pay special tribute to the many fallen heroes who gave their lives while serving others.

With all our love,

Nurse T, Timothy Sheard

Contents

ABOUT THIS DIARY

In March, 2020, as the Covid-19 virus ravaged the world, patients crowded the New York hospitals begging for treatment. Bodies piled up in temporary morgues outside the facilities. Despite the danger they faced, hospital workers went to work day after day, night after night, fighting for their patients' lives, and mourning the loss of those in their care.

Nurse T sent me a text message. She was alarmed by the horrific mortality rates in her Intensive Care Unit and across the New York region. The lack of effective treatments was deeply disturbing. Knowing that I am a writer and a publisher, she ended one text message with the words: "After this is all over, you've got to write a book about it!"

I replied, "No, Nurse T, we need to get these stories to the public *now*. They need to know what you are facing."

Together, we began documenting the conditions the staff and patients faced day after day, night after night. Several stories were published by Labor Press, for which we are deeply grateful. Together, we have tried to present the experience of Nurse T and her co-workers as honestly and accurately as possible. We hope these stories are comforting to these essential workers and are informative to the public.

IN THE ICU

March 25, 2020

When I walk through the automatic doors into the ICU at 7 AM, I step into a war zone. There are overflowing trash buckets and debris scattered all over the unit. Four red crash carts sit outside the rooms, their drawers open and largely empty, witnesses to the chaotic night. One of the patients who coded survived, the three others died. One body in a white plastic shroud is still in a room on the bed waiting for a stretcher.

I ask, "Why is the body still here?"

A weary night nurse tells me there are no stretchers to be had, all of them are in use holding bodies waiting for the trip to the temporary morgue – two refrigerated tents out in the hospital parking lot.

In normal times we might see 2-3 codes in our ICU in a month; now we see 4 or more in a day. Sometimes, *two at the same time.* Truly battlefield conditions.

I hear one of the night nurses yelling from inside a patient room at a young, baby-faced intern to come help, her patient is crashing and about to code. But the intern is afraid to leave his safe island in the doctor's report room, he knows that the Covid-19 virus is everywhere. Death's wings have scattered the virus like fine snowflakes over every computer keyboard and phone and countertop and chair in the unit.

As the ICU Attending and the Fellow join the nurse, the intern slowly follows them in, looking scared to death.

While the night nurse and the doctors are trying to save the patient who is crashing, I go into a small room that is cluttered with equipment. I cover my cotton scrubs with paper pants and a paper shirt, then I pull on a thick, long-sleeved cloth procedure gown and tie it snugly. I will wear the gown all day, hoping...praying it will keep me safe, and keep my family safe, when I return home.

I don an N95 "TB" mask, the only mask I will have to use for the twelve-hour shift, and follow it with goggles, a paper hat to cover my hair (already tied in a bun), and paper booties.

Standing outside the room of my first patient, the only survivor of the four night time codes, I put on a disposable isolation gown. It is a gown I will have to reuse for the whole 12-hour shift.

Outside the patient's room I take a deep breath...pause...open the door and step into a pool of bloody fluid. During the night the patient had pulled out his endotracheal (breathing) tube because they did not have enough of the sedating and anesthetic drugs to keep him asleep. There is no more Propofol or Versed, so we must go in the room every four hours or more and inject a dose of a 2nd or 3rd line sedative, hoping to keep the patient asleep. We will have to go back to Valium and Scopolamine if the shortage persists.

The patient came to the ER the day before with pneumonia in two of his lower lobes (bilateral basilar pneumonia). It is a classic Covid-19 presentation. Within twelve hours the pneumonia consumed all the lobes, whiting out the entire lung. He felt as if he was being held underwater drowning because he *was* drowning on his own pulmonary secretions and blood. So, he pulled out the endo tube hoping to take in one full breath of pure air. That was when he coded...and somehow survived.

After hanging new intravenous solutions and manually taking his temperature (the disposable automatic temperature probe that would normally display his temp on the heart monitor is out of stock), I ask our nurse's aide Lily to bring bags of ice. She hands them to me and I pack the bags of ice around his body to bring down the 104-degree fever. Satisfied, I remove the isolation gown, turn it inside out and stuff it into a plastic bag outside the room, ready to don it again with the next visit. By the afternoon when I put the gown back on for the umpteenth time, I will feel my own sweat clinging to the gown.

It is a sickening feeling.

Finally, the last dead body from the night is taken away. A housekeeper in a full hazmat suit comes in to clean the room. I can smell the bleach all the way to the nursing station. I say to my friend, Nurse O, "I wish the entire unit could be bathed continuously in the bleach solution."

Nurse O says, "Don't get me started on *my* wish list!" I can hear the exhaustion in her voice and see it in her eyes. Nurse O was born in Puerto Rico and grew up in New York. She gets tired when people ask, is she going to apply for US citizenship, she is a citizen by birth.

Nurse O is quiet and soft-spoken and has a lovely face, all the young doctors hit on her when they rotate through the ICU. Some of the

Attendings do, too, but she will be married in June...if the pandemic even allows for a ceremony.

At the head of our wish list, we want the hospital engineers to put fans in all the patient windows to blow the Covid-19 virus out into the wind where it will harmlessly dissipate, instead of letting it waft out into the ICU every time the door is opened. But the hospital has not approved the fans, we don't understand why.

We ask a Supervisor why they won't install the fans, other hospitals in New York have done it in all of their ICU rooms. She just shrugs. She doesn't know.

Providing enough PPEs so we didn't have to reuse ours over and over again would be nice. We're told not to expect more supplies any time soon, every hospital in the country is ordering them, the suppliers are out of stock. And to have enough first-line sedation and anesthetic drugs so our patients don't wake up and pull our their breathing tubes – that would be Heaven-sent. The Pharmacy doesn't know when the manufacturers will fill their orders. It may be days... or weeks...or months?

The ER nurse calls and yells in my ear. "Why is it taking so long to send my patient upstairs?

It's a madhouse down here, we have patients wall to wall and lined up in the street!"

I don't bother to defend myself, we are all working in the same hellscape – a scene a movie director could hardly imagine for the scariest horror movie ever.

A half-hour later Mr. G, the new patient, arrives. He is 45 years old. His skin is mortuary cold, his fingernails are gray instead of a healthy pink, and his blood sugar is 1800. I ask the ICU Attending, "Have you ever seen a blood sugar this high?"

Our Attending for the month is Dr. V. She is a veteran Pulmonary Care Physician who has seen it all. I always feel good when she's covering the unit. Dr. V tells me she has never treated a patient with a blood sugar that high before. She tells us they are learning that the Covid-19 virus wreaks havoc on diabetics. The current theory is that either the virus itself or the body's hyper-immune response makes the organs in the body resistant to insulin. Without insulin doing its transport job, glucose can't enter the cells, so it just builds up and up in the blood stream while the cells starve for nutrients.

With our fearless Nurse's Aide Lily helping, I settle the patient into the bed, adjust the intravenous infusions and tie his wrists to the bed frame to keep him from pulling out his breathing tube. Finally, I look for the first time into the man's face. It is a handsome face. It is a face that once laughed and smiled and winked at his children.

I know he will laugh no more, the cold ones always code, and they always die. I know that soon, probably during my twelve-hour shift, after another fruitless code I will have to drag the young intern out of his safe harbor to come pronounce the man 'dead.'

The hour waiting for a stretcher to remove the body will be when I get to eat my lunch.

In the nursing lounge at the end of the ICU I finally get a fifteen-minute lunch break – at 3 PM. I hurriedly gobble the last of my sandwich and gulp down a cup of lukewarm coffee. The thought keeps coming back to me: *how did we end up in such a mess? How come we weren't better prepared for the avalanche of patients that is crushing us?*

What went so very, very wrong?

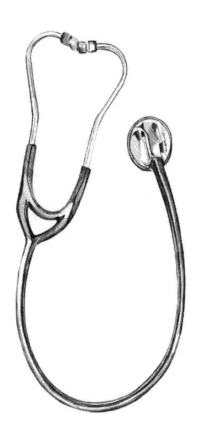

THE NEWS FROM CHINA

January 25, 2020

There is news on TV and in the papers about China, and it's scary as hell. There are reports of an outbreak, some kind of new ("novel") virus that is spreading across that gigantic country. They closed down Wuhan province – that's twenty million people – but it's the Chinese New Year, so millions of people are traveling to visit family, and many of them are going to other countries.

Am I crazy to think there's going to be a lot of people getting sick? The Chinese health authority is not giving out much information; they only report that they think this new coronavirus originated in one of their big open-air markets, where the farmers sell live animals. Pigs, chickens, marmots...even live *bats*. People working in the market and people buying food come into contact with the live animals, so there's a lot of cross-species transmission of bacteria and virus.

That's how a lot of viral outbreaks get started: from birds to pigs to humans.

Nobody in the US government seems too concerned about the outbreak right now. At least, not from what they are telling the press. But we've been through this movie before: remember the SARS outbreak in 2003? Or the Avian flu outbreak of 2014? That was a really *nasty* influenza virus; it was highly contagious and sometimes fatal ("Virulent"). I'm worried. Will this new "novel" virus come to our country? Will we see a flood of patients begging for treatment?

Today I asked our ICU Attending Physician, Doctor H, about the reports from China. He's a big bear of a man with a deep voice and a sweet smile. He likes to crack jokes on rounds in the ICU and keep everybody relaxed. Dr. H says he doesn't know much about this new virus either, just what's been in the press. He thinks we will be okay in the States, we have a strong federal public health system with the CDC (Center for Disease Control). He's not worried, but he's always the optimist.

I guess I'm just a worrier, but I can't help from picturing New York going through an epidemic like they have in Wuhan. Is our public health service really so much better than China's agency? That's what everyone says; I hope we don't have to test their faith in our system.

Later in the day the ID team ("Infectious Disease") comes into the unit on a consultation; a patient with a multi-drug resistant bacteria infection. He is on triple antibiotics, but so far, the infection is still out of control, we have to support the patient's blood pressure with intravenous drugs that raise the blood pressure ("pressors"). Basically, we're pumping adrenalin into his body around the clock.

The ID Attending, Dr. K, is rounding with his Fellow, Resident and Medical Student. He is a soft-spoken, balding gentleman who never loses his head; he's just the kind of doctor you'd want on your side in an emergency. Dr. K assures me that New York has one of the best public health departments in the country. They will institute hygiene measures that will prevent transmission of the virus, if it even shows up in the city, which is problematic.

I tell Dr. K I am hearing that the virus has spread across parts of China. That it sounds like a highly contagious pathogen. "Shouldn't we be preparing for it now?" I ask. He says we don't really have to worry until we see cases in the US, and so far, there have been no reports of any. He tells me when and if it hits New York, we will deal with it.

The ID team goes into the isolation room to see their consultation. There's a big sign on the door announcing" STOP – CONTACT ISOLATION PRECAUTIONS! The sign goes on to explain you must wear an isolation gown and gloves to approach the patient. Masks are not mandatory, since it's a bacterial infection, although some of us nurses wear a mask if we are going to have close contact with the patient, like bathing him or changing his bed. If he coughs on our face, it could expose our mucous membranes to the bacteria, which would be a pathway to infection for us.

Better safe than sorry. We put on an isolation gown and gloves, and then we mask up. I tell my friend Nurse O, who is caring for the patient with the drug-resistant infection, what ID said about the new virus. She is reassured, but still skeptical. "Well, at least we're used to dealing with isolated patients," she says. "I mean, it wouldn't be *that* much different from a flu patient with a secondary pneumonia, right?"

I want to agree with Nurse O, and with Dr. K, but a little voice inside my head is whispering, "Danger..."

An alarm sounds. One of my patients has dropped her oxygen level: she is "desaturating." I rush into the room, disconnect her breathing tube and attach an Ambu bag. I squeeze the bag and watch the patient's chest rise. I can see that the tube hasn't slipped out of place. I send a squirt of saline down the tube and suction out gobs of thick, yellow secretions, happy there is nothing blocking her tube. That would be serious. A blocked tube can be a disaster.

Hooked back up to the ventilator, my patient's oxygen level climbs back up to a normal level. I give her an extra dose of Fentanyl, the opiate we give by continuous infusion along with a sedative *and* an anesthetic. Fentanyl is like ten times more potent than morphine, so we really have to know how to dose it properly.

As I leave the patient's room, I see the ID Fellow standing at one of the portable computer stations completing his consultation. Then he trails behind the team as they make their way out of the ICU.

Nurse O sends Lily, our Nurse's Aide, to the Pharmacy to pick up the new antibiotic that was ordered on ID's recommendation. I ask Nurse O to cover for me and go the nurse's lounge for a cup of tea and fifteen minutes of quiet.

Even in the lounge, I'll be able to hear the alarms if my patient gets in trouble again.

I take out my cell phone and open it to the news.

The news is not good.

EUROPE IS IN TROUBLE

February 23, 2020

Now it's Italy that's in the news. The US President banned most airline travel from China to the United States because of the outbreak there, but cases of the Covid-19 virus – that's the official name, now – are showing up more and more in Europe. The President hasn't banned travel from those countries. I guess he doesn't want to anger voters with European heritage. Italy has the worst numbers, they are just *exploding* with cases, especially in the northern part of the country.

From Europe to New York is just seven or eight hours by plane. We get *so* many people traveling from there, and a gazillion New Yorkers go over every year. I can't understand why Europe isn't on the banned list. Or at least, Italy.

Oh my god, the World Health Organization has declared a global emergency, but the Mayor and the Governor don't seem to be doing

anything about it other than telling us we'll be fine, they are prepared for anything.

The CDC reported there are 35 confirmed cases in our country, but New York seems to be spared.

For now.

After taking report form the night nurse, I asked my Head Nurse if we should be doing anything to prepare for a possible outbreak. She tells me, "We have all the resources we need. And besides, it's not an American problem, it's in China."

"And Europe," I remind her. She goes away without a further word.

On morning rounds, I take Miss Q, the Pharmacist, aside to ask a question. She's a "Pharm-D," a Pharmacist with a PhD who rounds with the ICU doctors and advises them on the best drug regimens for their patients. Miss Q is a petite Asian American woman with big shining eyes and a glorious smile. She always speaks in a low, quiet voice, so sometimes the taller doctors have to bend down a tad to get every word.

I ask Miss Q if the Pharmacy is taking any special measures in case the Covid-19 cases start showing up here the way they are in Italy. She tells me as far as she knows, the pharmacy department hasn't done anything special. "But they can order overnight delivery of any medication we might need," she explains. "And the New York has containers filled with medications in strategic locations all across the state in case of emergency."

As far as she knows, New York is ready for anything. She rejoins the ICU team and I go to set up my antibiotics for the shift. That way, if things get hairy, I'll have everything lined up ready to connect to the IV line.

On my mid-morning break with Nurse O, I ask her what she thinks about the outbreak in China and Europe. She's a relatively new nurse, just five years out of nursing school, but her three years in the ICU have taught her more than most nurses learn in a lifetime. Nurse O wonders when we'll get an in-service on the new virus in Europe. "Maybe the Infection Control Department will come and give us a lecture and tell us what to expect," she says. "Or Infectious Disease, it's their area, after all." I wonder aloud if our Employee Health Service will bring us information, they're supposed to look after our health.

Somebody's got to know something! Every day, scores of planes land at JFK from Europe. And a lot of flights came from China up until the President's ban. Who knows if any of *those* passengers were bringing the virus to New York?

OUR FIRST COVID PATIENT

March 11, 2020

Well, it's finally happened: we admitted our first confirmed Covid-19 patient to the ICU today. Last month there were a bunch of cases in Washington State, and last week New York State saw its first confirmed case. It's a lawyer in the suburbs – Westchester – who tested positive. He was in close contact with a lot of people before he was put in isolation. Not just in his home town, either, he took the train into the City several times, so there could have been exposure there, the train is a closed environment, it's a perfect environment for carrying droplets laden with virus.

He worked in New York City, so there was opportunity to spread the virus here, as well.

Governor Cuomo declared a state of emergency a few days ago, we've had 89 confirmed cases in New York State. The Teachers union wanted the schools shut down, but the Mayor said "No," even though we are starting to see cases in New York. The children are riding the subways and the buses, potentially spreading the disease to grownups packed in with them.

Don't the politicians understand, this is a really bad, bad virus? Why doesn't the Mayor listen to the teachers? I just don't get it. He and the Governor seem to be playing some kind of macho word game. Why aren't they shutting down the city?

We're still waiting for an In-service program to inform us how to deal with this new virus. So far, nothing. We're pretty much on our own.

The Covid-19 patient, Mr. L, is a 77-year old man. He came to the ER with fever and chills and extreme shortness of breath, low blood pressure and rapid pulse, all signs of septic shock. His kidneys are failing too. His chest x-ray showed bilateral pneumonia. Reports from China and Europe say these are classic Covid-19 infection findings.

When we received the patient from the ER, we put him in our Negative Pressure Isolation room. That's the room with a fan in the window. Only two of our twelve ICU rooms have the fans. The fan blows room air out into the open air. That way, whenever anyone opens the door, air won't flow out of the room into the unit, potentially exposing staff (or other patients) to pathogens that ride the air currents. Pathogens like tuberculosis.

You might think it would be dangerous for the public to blow air laden with virus out into the community, but it is not. The virus quickly disperses and scatters in the wind, where it is harmless.

Nurse O is assigned to the patient. I go to help her settle the patient in bed. I put on an isolation gown and gloves. But when I root around in the isolation cart looking for an N95 "TB" type mask – the kind that traps tiny droplets ("aerosols") that contain the virus – I only find the basic surgical masks.

"Where's the N95 mask?" I ask my friend.

"Central supply didn't send them. The admitting orders only call for Droplet Precautions. The doctors say Covid isn't airborne, we don't need N95's."

"Are you *kidding* me?" I say. "It's a virus! We put patients with measles and chickenpox on airborne precautions..."

"Well, that's what the admitting orders say. Droplet precautions only."

"Huh."

I hurry to our own supply room and pull out a box of N95 masks to set on top of the isolation cart. We keep a small supply of them on hand in case one of our patients is suddenly diagnosed with an airborne pathogen and it's the middle of the night. In an emergency, like a code, you have to run in and you can't be bothered going down to Central Store to get the right masks.

We wear the N95 masks as we get the new patient settled and make sure his blood pressure and oxygen levels are compatible with life. We understand they aren't going to *be* normal. It seems, nothing will be normal with a Covid patient.

Later in the morning the ID team comes into the unit. They confer with our ICU team on the treatment plan for the Covid patient. Nobody knows how to treat this "novel" virus, it's a guessing game. They decide to continue the malaria drug and the antibiotic (Zithromax) that were started in the Emergency Room. The doctors are all serious and somber. It seems like they know more than they are letting on, or maybe they are feeling something they don't want to put into words.

Nobody wants to treat a disease that we have no effective treatment for. Even the aggressive cancers sometimes respond to chemo, radiation, immune-boosting drugs and such. But they don't have any good treatment for this Covid...no wonder the doctors are all grim.

I go to the ID Fellow and ask, "How come the new patient is only on Droplet Precautions. Don't you want Airborne precautions? Shouldn't we be wearing N95 masks?"

The ID Fellow, Doctor Q, is a Greek gentleman who speaks like a dozen languages. He's super smart, but humble. He tells me the information they are receiving is that Droplet Precautions are enough for Covid. He says they are "following the CDC guidelines."

That doesn't sound right to me, but I'm just a critical care nurse. It's not like I studied infectious disease in med school.

Nurse O continues to wear the N95 mask. The Head Nurse doesn't approve and warns her to follow the doctor's orders, but she just shrugs and tightens the N95 around her face.

You go, Nurse O! I say to myself.

I'm *so* proud of her.

Within twenty-four hours, the Covid-19 patient died. We could not get the oxygen level in his blood high enough to keep the organs functioning.

I'm getting scared, though I try not to show it, I have to set an example for the younger staff.

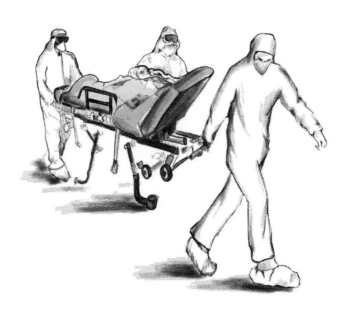

OUR COVID ICU

March 16, 2020

We have six Covid-19 patients in the ICU when I come on duty. They fill up half of our beds. Two died during the night. At first, we tried admitting Covid patients to one side of the ICU and the non-Covid to the other, but the Infectious Disease team thought the risk was too great of transmitting the virus across the unit ("cross contamination"), so now another ICU has the patients without the virus. We are basically "the" Covid ICU for the facility.

The population that we serve is largely Black and Hispanic. And poor. We have very busy clinics, which take all patients, nobody is ever turned away if they have no insurance or money to pay for services. They may not have any health insurance or they may be undocumented, but we care for them all.

When they become acutely ill, we admit them, no questions asked. Many have one or more chronic health conditions ("co-morbidities"), which complicates the treatment plan.

With the Covid-19 infection, it's beginning to look like they are more vulnerable than healthy people who enjoyed healthy diets and lifestyles, but no one is sure yet, the disease is just too new.

One nurse and our regular Housekeeper called out sick. I'm told there are sick calls in other departments as well. I hope to God they are not sick with the virus, that would be terrible, we have *no* effective treatment.

I ask our Head Nurse one more time when are we going to receive an in-service about how to care for these patients? But she doesn't know. She says nobody knows much about the disease anyway, so what would be the point of providing an in-service? Aren't we seasoned professionals who have cared for patients with communicable diseases before? She says there would be more questions than answers.

I get her point...I guess. But somebody has to know *something* about this pathogen. Don't they?

I ask her if Engineering is going to install negative pressure fans in the rooms that don't have them. I understand from a nurse who works in one of the prestige hospitals in Manhattan that they have installed fans in every one of their ICU rooms. My head nurse says she has not heard about any plans to put in fans, but she will let me know.

My two Covid patient are dependent on mechanical ventilators ("vents") to provide enough oxygen for their organs to function. And they are both on high doses of those adrenalin-like medications ("pressors") to keep their blood pressure high enough to pump an adequate supply of blood to the organs to keep them alive. Not that it's doing the kidneys much good, one patient is in complete renal failure, we are waiting for the Renal Service Team to insert a temporary catheter for dialysis. My second patient shows signs of renal insufficiency: the kidneys haven't failed, yet, but they are in trouble.

Lily brought me bags of ice cubes to pack around them, their fevers haven't responded to the non-steroidal anti-inflammatory drugs.

When a family member called and asked what are the visiting hours in the ICU, I had to ask Dr. V, the ICU Attending. She tells me, "I'm sorry, no visitors for now, we don't want to risk exposing them to Covid." That's a big change from our normal policy. Even with TB patients, family members were allowed to visit as long as they wore the N95 masks while in the negative pressure room.

I explain to the family member (a daughter) we have to restrict visitors for now, but she is welcome to call every day and the doctor will fill her in on the patient's condition.

Late in the morning the Head Nurse comes in and calls an impromptu meeting. She tells us she got a warning from the administration. They say we are using excessive amounts of PPEs – our personal protective equipment. We are going to have to reuse them for the entire twelve-hour shift.

I ask her won't that cause cross-transmission if we wear the same mask and gown and gloves for both of our patients? She looks at me like I'm an idiot. She says of course we have to change PPE's between patients. We will discard the gloves, but we will place our isolation gown and mask (*not* an N95!) in a plastic bag outside the patient's room. Then we put on a new set for the second patient, and when we go back to the first patient, we put the old ones on again.

Nurse O asks, "Is that safe? I mean, can you use the same mask for twelve whole hours?" The Head Nurse says she's just passing on what we are told. I ask why they won't send up N95 masks, why are they giving us just the flimsy surgical masks? Again, she says she is going by her instructions from administration. She finishes by reminding us NOT to post the Airborne Precautions sign on our patient's door, we only need to post the Droplet sign.

She gives me a dirty look as she turns to leave.

I look over at Nurse O as the meeting breaks up. She rolls her eyes and squeezes lotion onto her hands. They are getting irritated from so much hand washing and so much alcohol hand sanitizer use.

In the afternoon I page the Infection Control nurse who is covering the ICU. I tell her we are all scared because we aren't being given the N95 masks. We've already seen patients die from the infection. What does her supervisor say?

She tells me to the best of her knowledge, we only need Droplet Precautions for the Covid patients, so the N95 mask is not required. I ask her, "Does that make sense? It's a *virus*. Viruses are really, really tiny, they can float around in the air. Don't surgical masks fail to trap tee-ny-tiny droplets?"

Again, she tells me she is going by the information her supervisor gave her. We only need to implement Airborne Precautions when the patient undergoes a treatment that produces aerosols (tiny droplets), like when the Pulmonary doctor performs a broncoscopy (flexible tube down the airway).

I tell her that our patients produce aerosols *all the time*. Like when we administer pulmonary treatments to a patient on mask O2 (oxygen), or when we disconnect the endo tube from the ventilator, squirt saline down the tube to loosen secretions and do an open suction.

She admits I have a good point and promises to bring up my concerns at their monthly meeting. Infection Control meets with all the departments to discuss issues like this, so maybe a new directive will come out then.

I end by telling her other hospitals have made all of their ICU rooms negative pressure rooms, can't Engineering do that for us? She promises to let her supervisor know about my concerns.

I *hate* it when someone tells me I have to wait for the decision that will come out of a meeting. We need action today. *Right now.*

THE WAR ZONE

March 21, 2020

I can't believe it, when I come into the unit this morning, every bed in the ICU is occupied by a Covid patient. Yesterday we had three empty beds, this is c-razy. When I ask one of the night nurses how did we fill up so fast, she tells me the ER has *seven* patients waiting for an ICU bed, and there's at least one Covid patient in a Step-down room upstairs who needs to come down. Like, *STAT* ("life or death").

All elective surgeries are canceled, and all elective admissions for procedures are canceled. Cancer patients can't get in for their chemo or radiation treatments; dialysis patients can't get in to replace a catheter, they will have to go to another facility, if they can even be treated there. Many facilities want to know they will be paid for elective procedures, unlike our hospital, which treats everybody, regardless of ability to pay.

Welcome to my world.

My first patient coded in the ER and was revived, but she has not woken up. She has a gag reflex to the suction catheter when I gently push it down into her trachea to suck out thick, bloody secretions, that's a hopeful sign, and her pupils constrict to light. That's also hopeful. But she doesn't open her eyes to her name or squeeze my hand when I ask her to. She is limp, like a rag doll.

I'm giving her intravenous sedation, but at a low dose, in case she is awake "inside" and frightened. I know I would be. Besides, I don't want her to feel that sense of "suffocation" that patients on the ventilator feel, it's a terrifying sensation.

My other patient requires continuous heavy does of anesthetics and sedatives or he will pull his breathing tube out. He opens his eyes when I call his name but he doesn't follow any commands, he just kicks off the top sheet and tugs at his restraints. He has delirium with agitation, which is super difficult to control. It takes extra effort to breath through a narrow tube, it's feels like you are choking, so most patients instinctively want to pull the tube out. They don't understand that they need it to survive.

On morning rounds our Attending, Doctor H, asks me to page the Respiratory Therapist who is covering us, he wants to discuss some alternative ventilator settings. Dr. H is an Anesthesia and Critical Care Attending. Normally, the big man is in a good mood, but today he's grim, I can see the worry and the fatigue in his yes. He is frustrated that we aren't seeing better results in the blood gas reports. The Covid lungs are completely whited out on the X-ray. We can push one hundred per cent oxygen into their lungs and it isn't getting through the tiny air sacs ("Alveoli") into the blood.

Dr. H wants to try a really "out there" mode of ventilating one of my patients; the man who requires heavy sedation. Dr. H didn't *say* the woman patient who hasn't woken up is a hopeless case. Maybe I'm not reading his face correctly behind his mask when he discusses her case, but he looks like he's given up on her.

For the man, Dr. H wants to try what's called "inverse mode ventilation." Normally, when we breathe, the time we take to pull air *in* is about twice as long as when we breathe *out*. With the inverse mode, the ventilator rapidly pushes air into the lungs, then s-l-o-w-l-y lets the air come back out. It's a lot like holding your breath...

for every breath you take. He's hoping the extra time to exchange gases in the lung will help.

When ICU rounds are finished, the Resident, Dr. C comes to my room to implement the new ventilator mode. Dr. C is a tall Korean woman from the Anesthesia service who intends to go on to a Critical Care Fellowship after completing her residency. I like her, she's confident, but humble.

I page Miss B, the Respiratory Therapist. A few minutes later Miss B rushes into the ICU. She is a middle-aged woman with gray dreadlocks and a no-nonsense approach. She's all about getting the work done.

"Sorry I couldn't come right away," Miss B tells Dr. C "I had to replace the portable oxygen tanks on two ventilators in one of the Stepdown rooms."

I don't understand what the problem is. I ask Miss B why are they using oxygen tanks to supply a ventilator, why don't they use the forced air in the system that's piped all through the hospital.

"The hospital never replaced the low-flow pipes on the wards with the high flow ones you have in the ICU," she explains. "They can't supply enough pressure to run the vents, so we have to keep replacing the old school green tanks. It's a royal pain in the you-know-what."

I'm not surprised, just sad. We are a poor hospital serving a poor community. I'm sure the Department of Pulmonary Medicine and Respiratory Therapy have requested upgrading the oxygen delivery system for years, but money is tight, they have to pay the bills first, so the upgrades were never carried out.

Now the Step-Down rooms and even regular room are holding overflow ICU patients on ventilators. With old school green oxygen tanks.

The ICU Resident instructs the Respiratory Therapist on the new vent settings. The three of us stare at the patient's chest as it rises with a breath, stays inflated for what seems an eternity, then slowly falls as the breath is exhaled.

We look up at the oxygen level reading on the monitor above the bed. It doesn't go up at all. The Resident tells me the Attending doesn't have a lot of hope for the new mode, the patient's lungs are completely whited out on the x-ray. Oxygen just isn't transporting across to the blood. They don't have anything to stop this damned virus.

She looks down at her Smart watch, which has beeped. The color drains from her face.

"Oh my god," she whispers, loud enough for me to hear.

I ask what's wrong. She tells me she just received an alert from a program the Department of Health set up for New York City physicians. The alert says that a medical student who had just come back from a vacation in Italy tested positive for the Covid-19 virus.

I tell her that's such a shame. The resident explains, "That's not all. She was in another hospital working in the Operating Room. She was coughing *in* the OR. The senior Anesthesiologist didn't like the sound of the cough and sent her to the ER while the surgeon stopped the surgery. The student tested positive for Covid and they had to close the entire Emergency Department. The staff from the OR all went into quarantine."

The situation in New York City is starting to look like a nightmare. The kind you need to wake up from but it keeps on scaring you. I'm still trying to look calm and confident, but I suspect my feelings still show to those who know me. Even through the mask.

Later in the morning I check to see how my patient on "inverse" ventilation is doing. He's restless and pulling on his restraints, the prolonged expiration feels unnatural to him. I increase his sedation until he is calm, he's pretty much in an induced coma.

His oxygen level still hasn't improved on the inverse. In fact, it's getting worse. I try forcing oxygen into his lungs with the Ambu bag, but that doesn't help, either.

I report my patient's deteriorating condition to Dr. C, the Korean resident. She doesn't have any more tricks up her sleeve.

Our ICU is turning into a hospice. When the ward clerk calls out she has a family member on the phone asking for an update on their loved one, I don't have time to talk to them. It breaks my heart, but my patient's dropping oxygen level keeps me running back into his room.

The ward clerk reminds me, when my patient expires, they have patients in the ER waiting for the bed. She is young, sweet and anxious. She wears an isolation gown, gloves and mask for protection from the "Covid bombs" we release every time we open the door to a patient's room.

Meantime, there are four Covid patients in the Recovery Room all waiting for an ICU bed. Recovery is functioning as a temporary ICU, but the nurses there are not used to caring for unstable, critically ill patients, they are used to stable post-op cases who are on the way to the ward, or even to home.

When Dr. H and his team return from rounding on the patients in Recovery they go huddle in their on-call room. The ward clerk whispers to me to come to the desk. I walk over and ask her what's up?

"One of the Recovery nurses has been taken off duty," she tells me. "She heard Dr. H tell them they weren't going to take any of their patients, they are hopeless cases. He's saving our beds for the viable ones."

The clerk finishes by saying that the young nurse in Recovery broke down and could not stop crying when she heard Dr. H's words. The doctor covering Recovery wanted to admit her to the Psych ward, but it's filled with Covid patients, so they sent her home.

FEAR

March 28, 2020

We are all terrified.

Every nurse and doctor, every housekeeper and transporter, engineer and pharmacist – every worker stepping into the hospital knows they are risking exposure to Covid-19...risking severe illness for themselves and their families when they return home.

Risking death.

Sometimes I wonder how any of us summon the courage and the strength to return day after day, shift after shift, and put our bodies in the line of fire. We are on mandated overtime – four 1twelve-hour shifts in a row, so the hospital has put us up in a nearby hotel to sleep. Not that we sleep much, the trauma leads many of us to long, sleepless nights.

For many nurses like me, I come to work because it is simply my job. We live to serve the sick, just as nurses – "Medical Sisters" in olden days – have done for generations. We swore an oath when we earned our certificate or license. It is a sacred oath. It is the core of our profession.

Some of the hospital workers cope with the fear more effectively than others. Veteran nurses and experienced physicians have the greatest ability to control the terror, since we have encountered Death time and time again. The Grim Reaper is an old acquaintance of ours. Many a physician has labored over a patient in cardiac arrest, fighting in vain to bring the patient back. Many a nurse has washed the body, sealed the eyelids shut with a dab of lubricant, sprinkled oil of peppermint on the body to mask the foul odor, and folded the hands neatly on the chest, ready for the family to visit one last time before sealing up the body bag and sending it to the cold storage locker to await the undertaker.

Or the medical examiner.

Death is now let loose and raging through the hospital. His presence is more intense than any of us have seen before, but he is not a new visitor. During the pandemic I might assist in wrapping four bodies in one shift, rather than the one body in a week or a month from the old days, but the routine is the same.

Loyalty to our teammates also draws us back to work. As I walk past the temporary refrigerated tents in the street that are holding the overflow of bodies on my way to work, I smell a

putrid odor, the work of bacteria from the bowel feasting on the dead organs. I hurry past and enters the facility, taking the stairs to avoid the elevator and the co-workers crowded inside.

I couldn't bear to leave my comrades short-handed. It is an old taboo, strongly felt: to leave co-workers carrying a double assignment due to your absence is a shameful thing. Sometimes the hospital can't cover a call-out and a nurse coming off a twelve-hour night shift will be mandated to stay four more hours. My heart sinks when I see her wearily going back to care for her patients again.

You come to work to share the burden, you do not abandon your mates.

Staff members from other departments who do not normally care for terminal patients are less comfortable as they are reassigned and pulled into the maelstrom of the Covid-19 wards. For medical students recruited to patient care, the experience can shake them to their emotional core. Orders are yelled at them, they hurry to draw blood and rush it to the lab. They quickly assess new patients and report to their chief, or help a nurse to restrain a deliri-ous patient fighting for air. For life. The young doctor in training pushes a stretcher with a fresh body downstairs and out to the fetid temporary morgue. The lecture hall is a distant memory. An echo of academic times.

For the new medical and nursing graduates, it is baptism by fire: a decade of experience delivered in a week. In a day. An hour. For clerical staff unaccustomed to direct patient contact, it is a revelation, frightening but ennobling.

And so we return, exhausted but not defeated; terrified but undaunted. As the patient cries out for help, the caregiver manages a grim smile behind the mask and lays a gentle hand upon the suffering. The bond is strong, it cannot be broken.

Not even Death can sever it.

CAUSE OF DEATH

April 4, 2020

It is 10 AM and I am in Mr. P's room. I gently push the pliant plastic suction catheter down the endotracheal (breathing) tube in an effort to suck out the thick, bloody secretions that have choked the airways of the lung. The thick, tenacious secretions have filled the tiny air sacs that expand and contract with inspiration and expiration and have clogged the breathing tube. I cannot suction out any secretions, which means the ventilator cannot deliver the oxygen the patient needs to survive, even when the machine is set at 100% O2.

Mr. P is a 61-year old African American man with long dreadlocks, tattoos on his arms and an arterial-venous fistula where he used to receive kidney dialysis until he received a kidney transplant. As a transplant patient and a diabetic, his immune system is profoundly compromised due to the medications he takes to suppress rejection of the donated kidney. As a result he is unable to fight off the Covid-19 virus.

Mr. P's wife and three children have not been allowed to visit him since he was admitted to the medical ward, now essentially a Covid-19 unit. In fact, we have Covid patients filling all the wards and step-down rooms. We're an all-Covid facility now.

Two days ago, Mr. P transferred to the ICU with severe difficulty breathing, low oxygen levels in the blood and falling blood pressure. He was intubated and sedated. One of our Attending Surgeons – a stocky gentleman who loves to hunt and fish and "disappear into the wilderness" as he puts it -- came in with his Resident and inserted a central intravenous catheter in the femoral vein. His team has been inserting central lines all over the hospital. When they become clotted, which is happening more and more, they come back and replace the catheter over a wire. They are an efficient team, and a godsend.

The ventilation system forms a closed seal, so when the I snake the suction catheter down the endo tube I can suck out the secretions without releasing droplets into the air. The staff makes every effort to minimize dispersion of droplets, knowing they will drift out of the room when the door is opened – the "Covid bomb." When I leave the room I will be dusted with virus if the seal of the ventilator is broken.

During the night the pharmacy ran out of Fentanyl, the primary opiate infusion we use to sedate the patient. Morphine is also gone, as is the primary anesthetic Propofol and the sedative Midazolam. For the first two hours of my shift I have struggled to keep my patient calm with intermittent injections of Ativan, but this drug, too, is in desperately short supply, and I just don't have enough to keep the patient sedated.

Half-awake and mad with the feeling of suffocation that his drowning lungs produce, the patient starts to breath rapidly. His respiratory rate is in the 50's – so rapid and shallow that he never takes in any fresh air. This makes the feeling of drowning even worse.

Mr.P'sheartrateclimbsto150...160..170..180! At this rate the heart hasn't time to fill during the relaxation phase of the cardiac cycle. Its output drops to a miniscule volume. His blood pressure falls down...down... down.

I am desperate to get oxygen into his lungs. I disconnect the ventilator tubing from the breathing tube and attach the Ambu bag. I vigorously squeeze the bag while the ventilator alarm sounds, but still I cannot force oxygen into the patient's lung. The distal (end) portion of the tube is completely blocked.

I yell for the crash cart. As Nurse O and the ICU Resident rush into the room, I explain that I can't suction the patient or get oxygen down the tube with the Ambu. Soon the whole critical care team is squeezed into the cramped ICU room and the ICU Fellow begins compressing the chest.

The Fellow (who had been home sick with Covid-19 and is now hopefully immune) suggests pulling the endo tube and replacing it with a larger #8 bore. Dr. C, the Anesthesia resident, is doubtful, they usually don't like fat tubes, fat tubes can erode the trachea, which leads to devastating complications. But Dr. V, the ICU Attending, nods to the ICU Fellow to go ahead.

Hurriedly, I pull the new "fat" tube from the red crash carts. I rip open the packet with the black stripes confirming it has been sterilized and hand it to the Fellow. After removing the current breathing tube, the Fellow visualizes the airway and deftly slides the new "fat' tube into place. I inflate the little pilot balloon that will seal it in place and quickly secures the tube with tape.

We work on the patient, giving oxygen, compressing the chest manually, shooting drugs into the bloodstream to try and elevate the blood pressure, but we all know the effort is useless. Mr. P had grown cold, his transplanted kidney had ceased to function, and his other organs were failing as well.

Dr. V calls off the code. She promises to call the family to notify them of the death. The team members rip off their isolation gowns and exit the room, leaving me to clean the patient and prepare him for transfer to the makeshift morgue out in the parking lot, which is over-flowing with bodies, the undertakers can't handle the heavy case load.

Lily comes in, tying up her isolation gown and pulling a clear visor like the one welders wear over her face, already covered by her P100 mask. It is even better than the N95 mask. The Critical Care Division paid for them out of their own budget. When the masks arrived, one of our nurses and the ICU Fellow went down to Central Stores and asked for them. At first, the clerk denied even having them, but then she found the boxes. They brought them unopened to the ICU. We were like kids on Christmas morning when we opened the boxes and unwrapped the heavy-duty reusable masks with replaceable fil-ters. Oh, the feeling of security we all had when we strapped them on! What a relief!

I silently wipe the secretions off Mr. P's face and chest while Lily washes his chest. There is nothing to say. No words can express our sorrow. We don't speak to or look at each other, we just go about the routine of post mortem care. I think about the reports that are coming in that poor patients – especially Black and Hispanic patients – are way more likely to die from Covid than their White counterparts. Their poverty has given them multiple co-morbidities, like diabetes, hypertension, obesity and asthma.

In my silence I wish the Attending Physician could write in the death certificate under cause of death: *hospital poverty due to refusal of the gov't to provide adequate resources and staff for impoverished patients of color.*

When we are done preparing the body for transport, I finally leave the room and page the morgue attendant. The attendant calls back and asks if I have heard the news. What news? Mr. E., an African American nurse tech in the Recovery Room, has died in one of the other ICU's. He was the sweetest, kindest, gentlest man I ever worked with.

His wife is in a coma in the next bed.

I hang up the phone.

I am too forlorn to cry.

LILY

April 6, 2020

Lily is a veteran nurse's aide with over twenty years of hospital duty behind her. She is a short strong woman, just five foot three inches tall, but she is toughened by her years of working in the ICU. When you deal with angry families, impatient doctors, indifferent administrators and the wear and tear of working three 12-hour shifts in a row – sometimes, over a weekend – you either change your occupation or develop a thick skin and a strong voice.

Even when every bed in our ICU has a Covid-19 patient in it, Lily continues going to work. She is an asthmatic and knows that the virus attacks the airways and the lungs. Her husband wanted her to stay home because of her asthma. He was worried about exposing the children, too, they have a young daughter and a son. But Lily promised to be careful. Her husband has a good union job, he works as an elevator repair-man, and in New York they are *always* busy.

Every day when she comes home from work, she leaves her clothes in the outside hall in a

covered bin. She takes a long shower, and she sleeps on a cot in a little nook off the kitchen.

When Lily was caring for Covid-19 patients in the ICU, there were not enough masks, not enough isolation gowns, not enough isolation rooms and not enough sedating medications. With half the housekeeping staff out sick and hotel housekeepers laid off all around the city, the administration is refusing to hire temps from an agency to replace them, so the aides and the nurses have taken up much of the cleaning.

On her latest weekend, there were only three housekeepers on duty on the day shift for the *whole hospital,* the supervisor couldn't explain why. Lily knew that the entire intensive care unit is covered with the virus. Countertops, telephones and computer keyboards, door handles and rolling computer stations are all contaminated. She wipes down her cart and the nursing station counter top at the start of her shift, knowing Covid is in the air and raining down all around her.

How long will the just-disinfected surface stay clean? Lily looks up from her work as a doctor opens the door to one of the ICU rooms. Because there is no fan blowing the Covid-laden air out into the wind, the virus wafts out through the open door into the unit. We call it a 'Covid bomb."

Lily wearily takes out her disinfectant spray and starts again.

Then Lily began to feel the aches. Not the aching feet and knees from long hours on her feet, but muscle aches that wash over her whole body; the "myalgia" characteristic of a viral infection.

A Covid-19 infection.

The next day she visited her primary physician, who prescribed Tylenol, ibuprofen and plenty of liquids. She went home to rest.

That night, Lily's temperature reached 102. She had chills that would not abate, even after taking the non-steroidal over-the-counter meds. Her breathing was labored and she was wheezing. The rescue inhaler helped some, but did not restore normal breathing. Her husband sat up with her, even though she begged him to get some sleep.

The next day her husband drove her to the Emergency Department. He had to say good-bye at the ramp. Every nursing staff member knows that a Covid-19 infection could well be fatal, especially for an asthmatic. The hospital had to set up two temporary morgues – refrigerated tents in the parking lot – just to handle all the corpses.

Lily's temperature in the ER was elevated and her pulse was over 100. Her chest X-ray showed infection at the base of one lung (left-basilar pneumonia), the classic finding in Covid-19. Her physical exam revealed wheezing upon taking a deep breath, and her oxygen saturation, even while receiving oxygen, was only 80% – well below the expected level of 100.

Since she was stable on simple oxygen delivered through her nose by cannula, they admitted Lily to a medical ward. By now it was nearly midnight. The kitchen was long closed, but a kind nurse on the ward gave her a can of liquid nutritional supplement and a cup of hot tea with lots of sugar: calories to hold her until the morning.

Throughout the night, Lily suffered multiple panic attacks. No family members were allowed to be with her. Overhead she heard the hospital operator calling a cardiac arrest. The announcements seemed to come every hour all night long. She knelt on the floor beside her bed, trying to catch a full breath and struggling to hold back the panic. She prayed to the Lord that the hospital operator would not call her room number. She was terrified that a young physician or medical student would soon be compressing her chest as she lay pulseless and unconscious on the bed.

Lily slept not a wink that night. The float resident on call ordered an anti-anxiety medication to calm her, which helped her get through the long graveyard shift but still brought no slumber.

In the morning, a respiratory therapist came by and measured her oxygen saturation with a portable monitor. Lily's level had risen to 90% - an encouraging sign. The number calmed her. Maybe her condition would not deteriorate. Maybe she would survive. After breakfast she slept. No nightmare disturbed her sleep.

I was not allowed to visit Lily, which broke my heart, but the only persons allowed onto her ward were the staff assigned to work there. Even the dietary aides who brought up the meal carts had to leave the food outside the entrance to the ward. I texted her several times a day, and I kept in close contact with Dr. V, our ICU Attending.

Doctor V checked in on Lily *every day*, and she's consulted with the Medical physician, as well as the ID Fellow. She is the most caring, competent and resourceful physician I could ever wish to work with. Doctor V explained to Lily that she would breathe more easily if she lay on her stomach ("prone") part of the time. We called it "proning the patient." Lily tried it, and it did make her feel more comfortable. It probably saved her from having the breathing tube inserted in her airway...or worse.

On her third day on the ward, Lily was s-l-o-w-l-y improving and becoming less frightened. She allowed her children to "visit" by cell phone Facetime. I learned later that her husband cried every time he finished one of the "visits," but never in front of the children.

We sent Lily treats to keep her spirits up: cake and fresh fruit, baby powder, fluffy sox and pink slippers with sparkle on them. That cheered her up. As long as we were not getting a report that she was coming to the ICU, we were hopeful.

Discharged after a week on the ward, Lily is recovering at home. She has to stay away from her husband and the children, which is *so* hard for her. But they all know it is to keep them safe. She is anxious to donate her blood serum to provide precious antibodies to the infected patients waiting for beds in the ER or falling into septic shock in the ICU.

I call Lily at home when I finally get time to grab a sandwich sent up from the kitchen, we don't have time to leave the ICU now and we don't want to spread the virus that's clinging to our shoes, our hair...to everything.

Lily is eager to return to work, although nobody really knows how long the virus could remain in her body. But when she *does* return, she will be one of the invincible warriors, immune –she prays – to the virus, able to step in when the patient becomes delirious and fights to get out of bed or pull out the breathing tube. She will be unafraid of exposure, confident in her skills, fortified by her faith and by her love of nursing.

THE GOOD FRIDAY MIRACLE

April 10, 2020

On Good Friday, I walk up the ramp to the Emergency Room and enter the hospital to start my shift. I hope that today it may be different. "This is going to be a better day," I tell myself. I have prayed for relief, not so much for myself, but for my patients. I've seen that the mortality rate of intubated patients in our ICU is 50% - "as deadly as the Bubonic Plague was in the Middle Ages." Things have to get better... *don't they?*

Yesterday, a Covid-19 patient on the medical ward became acutely short of breath, with an oxygen saturation in the low 80's. She had a nonproductive (dry) cough, chills and fever. The physician tried to support her breathing with an external positive-pressure mask (Bipap). It is much like the mask that people suffering from sleep apnea wear during the night. But the Bipap failed to raise the patient's blood oxygen level. At noon she was transferred to the ICU for sedation and intubation.

My heart sank when I took report on the patient Thursday afternoon. Miss C is one of the floor nurses. She is a shy, quiet woman who has given or taken report from me countless times over the years. I silently vow to fight my hardest for one of our own. I know it could easily have been me or one of my co-workers admitted to the ICU fighting for breath.

The intubation in the ICU went smoothly. I pushed a sedating drug through the IV tubing, immediately giving Miss C the gift of sleep. The Anesthesiologist, a Russian gentleman with a three-day beard and a calm manner, made the procedure look easy. The patient's oxygen level slowly rose as the ventilator pushed against the resistance of "stiff lungs" – airways inflamed by the invading virus.

Because Miss C requires only light sedation, I am able to talk to her. I try to encourages her, saying, "Concentrate on breathing slow and deep, and stay strong, we are here for you, you're going to make it!" Miss C nods her head, trying to believe my words, but I can still see the fear in her eyes.

I adjust the light sedation and step out of the room. We nurses have loudly and bitterly complained for weeks that we have not received extra-long IV extension tubing. Using the old tubing, we must go into the isolation room whenever we have to adjust the intravenous solution's rate of flow, replace an IV bag or hang a new medication. Often, we must access the IV line and push a sedative or narcotic directly into the blood stream to rapidly suppress delirium and agitation. And each time we open the door we release that "Covid bomb" because we don't have fans in the windows blowing the virus out of doors.

When I return to work the next day, Friday morning, I am surprised and relieved to discover the extended IV tubing arrived late on Thursday night. The IV pumps are now positioned outside the room, so I am able to adjust them or inject IV meds without entering the room, minimizing my exposure to the Covid-19 virus and minimizing release of virus into the unit.

That one simple improvement lifts my spirits. I suddenly feel like a Super Nurse. "I will save all my patients! I will defeat the Grim Reaper!" I declare. The gaggle of doctors rounding in the unit turn and stare at me like I'm crazy, then continue with their rounds.

Even the rate of admissions to the ICU has dropped, the ER sending only one patient that morning. Miracle of miracles!

The night nurse gives me the best news of all: she was able to wean Miss C off her sedation. The patient's oxygen level is stable, she is awake and calm and waiting to be extubated. She is the first Covid-19 patient to be purposely extubated that I have cared for over the last two weeks.

I suit up with four layers of PPE, don my face mask and goggles and lower the face shield over my head, a generous gift from one of the New

York area unions. The union donated 5,000 priceless shields. I open the door and slip into the room.

When Miss C sees me, she wiggles her fingers, motioning for me to come closer. Both her wrists are restrained for her safety, because too many patients are pulling out their breathing tube out of desperation to just breathe. Hesitating at first but looking at Miss C's bright eyes, I step to the bedside, lean closer and tell her, "We are getting that tube out today, and I'm going to help you keep it out!"

A few minutes later the ICU Fellow and a Respiratory Therapist enter the room. They remove the breathing tube safely and switch her to a high flow nasal cannula. Her first words are, "Thank you!" Tears of joy run down Miss C's face. I cannot hold back my tears as well.

A truly Good Friday. "Thank you, Lord," I whisper to myself as I exit the room. I remove my outer, 4th layer isolation gown and stuff it into a plastic bag so it can be reused over and over. I pull off my gloves and mask and go to wash my hands.

I know not to touch my eyes to wipe away the tears.

THE TEDDY BEAR

April 14, 2020

I am shaky. I feel weak. It is nine hours into a twelve-hour shift and I haven't had lunch or even a coffee break. My legs are wobbly. Finally, I get fifteen minutes in the nurse's lounge, where Nurse O, a co-worker, is wolfing down pizza donated by a local business. I wipe down the chair and the table surface, settle in and grab a slice thick with roasted vegetables and jerk chicken. It is Heaven-sent and I already feel a little better, in part because I know there are people in the community who are supporting us, even if it's something as simple as a pizza.

"You know what I miss?" I ask my friend.

"A real lunchbreak?" Nurse O replies.

"That, too, sure, but I miss the families. I miss hearing about my patient from them, when they're sedated and they can't tell me themselves."

"Mmm, yeah, I miss that, too. There's no time to even talk on the phone to them, we're running around like machines. Yesterday I had four patients, and they were all unstable!"

"Robots," I reply. "We've become robots. We can't even speak to the family on the phone anymore, we're just running all the time. It's *terrible*."

ICU nurses are used to encountering death, but not so many dying in a day. Not so many unstable, septic (infected in the blood) patients. And not so many patients attacked by a disease we don't understand. Even when a patient's breathing tube is removed and we *could* talk, we have no time to sit and answer questions; no time to comfort and reassure. The traditional connections between nurse and patient and nurse and family are severed. It is an essential part of the nurse's role and is critical for the patients and family as well.

Finishing my slice, I get ready to go. "I hope Mr. W, makes it," I say. "He reminds me of a big teddy bear."

"A three-hundred fifty pound teddy bear," says Nurse O

Mr. W has been in the ICU and sedated for 18 days. He has a psych history. I suspect he had a developmental disability as a child, but the history is unclear.

On his third day in the ICU he pulled out his endotracheal (breathing) tube when the sedation wore off, the pharmacy had run out of the drugs needed to keep the patient unconscious. He coded and was revived. Today, his oxygen levels have improved to the point where the Critical Care Attending is hoping to extubate him (remove the tube).

On rounds outside Mr. W's room, the ICU Attending nods to the Fellow, who gestures to the respiratory therapist. I follow them into the isolation room. I have been reducing the patient's IV sedation gradually over several hours. He is now awake enough to trigger the ventilator. When I approach the bedside, he half-opens his eyes and looks into my face.

"Mr. W, we're going to take the tube out of your throat now, okay? Just lie still, it will be all right."

As I loosen the tape that secures the tube, the Anesthesiologist deflates the little pilot balloon that helps anchor it in the airway. He pushes the closed-suction catheter down to catch any loose secretions, gently pulls out the tube and drops it in the waste basket.

I quickly switch the patient to a mask and turn up the flow of oxygen. I elevate the head of the bed to help Mr. W expand his chest, then I release the restraints that held his arms down.

"Please don't pull on any of your tubes, okay?" I say, gently placing my hand on his shoulder. "You could hurt yourself if you do."

Mr. W looks around the room. Looks at the masked and gowned caregivers putting away their instruments and stepping out of the isolation room. His face betrays his confusion: he does not know where he is or who the people in the masks and strange outfits are.

Just as the doctors leave the room, Mr. W begins to yell and scream. He kicks his legs out from under the top sheet and shifts them over the edge. He pushes down into the mattress, trying to pivot his great 350-pound body so he can sit on the edge and get to his feet. I rush into the room with Nurse O right behind me and grab Mr. W by the shoulders. I know he is too big for me to lift him if he collapses onto the floor.

"No, no, Mr. W! You can't get out of bed yet, you're not strong enough. Please, sit back!"

A fresh look of fear on his face, he reaches to the oxygen mask and tries to lift it away from his face. "Where am I?"

I gently press his hand down onto the bed. "You were on the breathing machine for 18 days! We had to sedate you, you had a Covid infection!"

"I had the virus?" The situation slowly dawns on him. The confusion in his eyes begins to clear. "Wow. I had the virus..."

"Yes, but you're *strong,* you're getting *better.* That's why you have to stay in bed. If you fall down you'll be in the hospital a whole lot longer, and we're just nurses, we couldn't pick you up if you fell. Okay?"

"Okay, yeah, okay." He settles back into the bed and closes his eyes. His face is calm, his breathing, regular. I look up at the monitor and sees his oxygen level is 90 – a good sign.

Nurse O says, "Your brother Raymond called, I told him you were doing much better. He sends his love."

Mr. W nods his head and smiles a little piece of happiness. "Okay, now I know where I am."

As we straighten out the sheets and tuck them in at the foot of the bed, Mr. W asks if he can hear a song. There is no TV or radio in his room. Nurse O hums a little tune. Mr. W says, "No not that, something with rhythm. Bobby McFerrin."

Nurse O begins to sing, "Don't worry...be happy..." Mr. W and I join in, all swaying to the song. He has a big smile on his face.

When my co-worker goes out, I ask, "How about a nice back rub?" He smiles. I work the controls on the bed and it begins to massage his back. The bed has a series of motors that rhythmically press against the mattress. The treatment helps loosen secretions in the lungs as well as soothe sore muscles. As the massage calms the patient, he relaxes into the bed.

I tiptoe out of the room as if leaving a sleepy child at nap time. Removing my outer PPE, I softly sing, "Don't worry...da-da di da... be happy..."

PUTTING OUT FIRES

April 15, 2020

This is the story of a courageous young traveling nurse who came from Wyoming to work in our hospital during the pandemic – Nurse Y She is slim, blonde, blue-eyed and has a sweet smile. She was paid $3,000/week to come and work, which is good money for any nurse, but especially good for a nurse from a rural, western state. Nurse Y stayed in the hotel where other staff members were sequestered, but in her case, she could not go home when she had four or five days off.

It was a lonely time for her. A challenging time. I'm sure it changed her. I know it changed me.

Today, Nurse Y is taking report on two patients. It is her third day working in our ICU. Nurse O has been assigned to mentor her, we're not sure how much critical care experience the young nurse has had.

The morning seemed to start okay, even though I had three patients and both of Nurse O's patients were unstable, with falling oxygen levels and getting maximum intravenous pressors (adrenalin). One had coded during the night and survived, but now she is in a coma. Dr. V, the ICU Attending, doesn't expect her to wake up.

At just after ten, Nurse O's post-code patient went into cardiac arrest, but at the same time, Nurse Y's patient started dropping *his* blood pressure and threatening to code. His oxygen level on the monitor was drifting down...down...down.

While the ICU Fellow and a medical student were performing CPR on her coding patient, Nurse O ran over to the room to check on the young traveling nurse. Nurse Y was crouched in the corner outside her patient's room with her knees pressed to her chest. She was trembling and her face was as pale as a bed sheet.

"Miss Y, what are you doing? Your patient is crashing!"

"I know!" Nurse Y cried. "I don't know what to do."

"Haven't you worked in an ICU before?"

Nurse Y shook her head. "No, never."

"What about step-down? Telemetry? Emergency Room?"

In tears, the young nurse form Wyoming confided that she'd just graduated from nursing school. This was her first full-time job. "I did work all through school as a nursing assistant!" she added.

It turns out Nurse Y's family was in desperate financial condition. Her father and mother had both been laid off due to the pandemic. Nurse Y was the youngest of the children, and she was asked to keep the family afloat so they did not lose their home. So, she accepted the offer to work in New York City and fudged her work experience a bit.

Actually, she fudged it a whole lot.

She is still trying to convince her family that the Covid-19 pandemic is not a hoax, they have not seen many cases in Wyoming and they think it's all a liberal east coast conspiracy.

"Okay, okay, you have to stay calm," Nurse O told her. "Remember you're A-B-C's and you can't go too far wrong. Remember? The *basics*."

"Right. I know that: Airway...breathing...circulation."

"Good. Check the vent, check the tubing, Ambu and suction."

Nurse O hurried back to her coding patient to pull the drugs from the crash cart and inject them as the doctors struggled to restart the heart. One of my three patients had somehow gotten a hand free from the restraints (we can't make them *too* tight or they block the circulation to the hand and the tissues die) and was pulling on the breathing tube. I was desperately trying to loosen his fingers from the tube and get the arm back down to restrain it, so I couldn't help Nurse Y with her patient.

Once the Attending called off the code and pronounced the patient 'dead,' Nurse O was able to check on her young charge. Nurse Y reported she had suctioned out a big clot and a "ton of mucous." That had raised the patient's oxygen reading and raised his blood pressure as well. For the moment, the crisis was passed.

"Have you got your backup drips mixed and ready to hang? If the epi runs out and you don't have the next bag on the pole ready to spike, he'll lose his blood pressure big time."

"Right: backup intravenous. Got it."

For the whole twelve-hour shift, Nurse O shuttled back and forth between her patients (the ER sent her a new admission as soon as the room was cleaned, of course) and Nurse Y's assignments. The patient plugged his ventilator tubing several more times, but Nurse Y was able to clear the tubing and prevent a full code.

"Their coagulation is totally disturbed," Nurse O explained to the young nurse. "That's why we have them on anticoagulant therapy, although it doesn't seem to be helping all that much."

At the end of their shift, Nurse O and Nurse Y rode together to the hotel. I had finished my "four in a row," so I was allowed to go home, where I dropped my clothes in a separate bin, showered and shampooed, and put on fresh clothes. My towels went in a separate bin that my dear husband handled. Wearing gloves and a mask (but not an N95!), he threw all my clothes and towels in the washing machine in the basement. That's where he is sleeping now, as I need to sleep alone in our bed.

When I come out of the shower, dressed and clean, my boy asks if he can hug me now. I assure him it's safe and he gives me a big hug that washes away the fatigue.

Over my late dinner (hubby fed the kids and himself already) I thank the Lord that the new graduate from Wyoming had such a patient teacher in Nurse O. Nurse Y will one day return to her home town when we finally "flatten the curve" and lower our infection rates way, way down. And she'll be ready for anything: for the coronavirus; for cardiac arrests; for back-to-back twelve-hour shifts. She'll be battle tested. She'll be big city ICU tough.

Lying alone in bed, I closed my eyes and imagined my family and me on a beach somewhere. Hawaii, maybe, with no Covid-19, no fears, no restrictions.

Will we ever get to Paradise?

I fell asleep, the stress and tension of the day erased for a few blessed hours of sleep.

BLOOD POISON

April 16, 2020

It is two hours into my shift and I am frustrated like nobody's business. The Infection Control Nurse has made her rounds. She is caring and diligent, but she doesn't make the rules. I ask her if the administration ever approved installing fans in the ICU rooms that don't have them so they would all be negative pressure rooms. She tells me there is a big plan for major infrastructure upgrades "in the works" but they will have to wait until after the pandemic.

I tell the Infection Control Nurse that we need the fans installed in the rooms *today*. This morning. Right now. I remind her about the Covid bombs we set off every time we open the door. She is sad and discouraged. Her Supervisor advocated for them in their monthly meeting, but he was turned down, nobody seems to know why.

I had heard from a medical Resident who completed a month-long Infectious Disease rotation that the ID Department wanted N95 masks used from the beginning, but they had been overruled, there just weren't enough of the high filtration masks in stock to supply the whole staff. When I run this by the Infection Control nurse, she says, "You know more than I do, my dear."

Our talk is interrupted by a ventilator alarm sounding. One of my patients has pulled out her endotracheal (breathing) tube. The woman's oxygen saturation displayed on the overhead heart monitor is dropping...dropping down into the 70's, even though she is on 100% oxygen. But I have been wrestling with another agitated, delirious patient, the shortage of sedating drugs is making it impossible to keep him calm, and I am unable to intervene in the other patient.

Desperate to breathe, she has freed one of her hands from the cloth restraint and yanked out the tube. Cardiac arrest was imminent.

It is her third time pulling out the breathing tube. As I yell for the doctors to come and re-tube the patient, I wonder how many times the patient can survive pulling out her endo tube. The medical team hurriedly don their isolation PPE's and rush into the cramped room, where they find the patient gasping open-mouthed, starving for air like a fish out of water, even with the temporary mask delivering oxygen that I have pressed on her face.

With sedation in extremely short supply, the Anesthesia resident, Dr. C, a tall, British gentleman with an accent that makes me smile, elects to administer a paralyzing agent. The paralytic immediately renders the patient limp and immobile, but inside, the woman is awake and terrified as her mouth is pulled open and the new tube is pushed down her trachea (airway).

While the Brit secures the new tube, I examine the old one. It is clogged with solid blood clots. I show them to the Anesthesiologist and ask, "What the Hell is going on with the patient's blood?"

He offers (in his lovely accent) a diagnosis that frightens even a veteran like me. "D-I-C." Disseminated Intravascular Coagulation.

Leaving the patient's room, Dr. V, the ICU Attending, gathers her team around the sink. She is a short, heavy-set woman with dark, close-cropped hair and dark eyes that once were mischievous but now only show fatigue and sorrow. As the doctors wash their hands one at a time, Dr. V asks, "Do you know what happens when you are bit by the Black Mamba snake?"

The British doctor, who has studied tropical medicine, answers. "The toxin sets off the blood's clotting mechanism. Clots form throughout the vascular tree. Death occurs within minutes." The Attending confirms that the Covid-19 virus has an effect similar to the bite of the Black Mamba snake: it sets off a coagulation cascade inside the patient's body.

With all hands clean and dry, Dr. V leads the group to a computer and shows them images of a clot in the carotid (neck) artery of a Covid patient, captured by a sonogram, and another of multiple clots in a heart chamber. Everyone is dazed and in shock.

I tell the Attending that when I checked the patient's urine output on her hourly assessment, I found blood clots in the urometer, I had to milk the foley tube to get the urine to flow.

The Attending orders a blood "thinner" – a drug that interrupts the body's clotting mechanism. It is normally given to patients with pulmonary emboli (blood clots in the lung) or phlebitis (clots in the leg). She isn't confident that the drug will be effective, nobody understands how the virus disrupts the body's clotting mechanisms. Nor does she know how it can disrupt the peripheral nervous system and suppress the sense of taste and smell, but it does. Still, she reflects, they are beginning to develop treatment strategies, hoping to lower the devastating mortality rate.

I ask Dr. V if she is going to order Remdesivir. It's an established anti-viral drug that's showing some effectiveness in fighting the coronavirus. She tells me she asked for the drug for several of our patients, but it's not yet available in the pharmacy, she doesn't know why.

A moment later the hospital operator calls out a Code Blue on the loudspeaker overhead. It is on one of the medical wards. At the moment the ICU has no empty beds to receive the coding patient, although a bed is likely to open up when another patient dies. Wearily, the Attending sends the Anesthesiologist and an intern out to the ward to assist with the code.

She does not know where they will find a suitable critical care bed to receive the patient. If my patient pulls out her breathing tube again and expires, I will likely admit the code from the ward.

TEARS

May 7, 2020

I am driving to work, my co-worker Nurse O in the seat beside me. We have left the hotel where the city has been putting us up between shifts. It is a cloudy, gray day; Spring has been late and there has been much rain. "Much weeping in the heavens," Nurse O says.

As soon as we spy the roof of the hospital, Nurse O breaks into tears. I park the car and sit silently, waiting for my friend to finish.

"Ready?" I finally say.

Nurse O dabs her eyes with a tissue and nods her head. She exits the car and walks toward the hospital as if going to a hanging.

When we enter the ER, we spot Nurse A., a sprightly young nurse from India. Nurse A. had rotated through the ICU during her orientation. Everyone liked her and wished she would work with us in the ICU.

"How is Mr. B.?" the ER nurse asks. "I admitted him last week. Such a lovely man. So big and healthy looking." Mr. B. is six foot, two inches tall and built like a linebacker. He has no chronic health conditions.

Nurse O tells me the doctors do not expect him to survive. She slowly shakes her head in sorrow. She recalls how the man came to the ER two weeks ago with mild, flu-like symptoms. The physician saw that the man did not have a high fever and was not short of breath. He assured the physician he was not having any difficulty breathing, except when he exerted himself too much. The ER doctor sent the patient home, saying, "Come back if you feel worse."

Four days later, Mr. B. became weak and extremely short of breath. His wife called 911. As the paramedics wheeled him up the ramp to the ER., he waved to his wife and son, who were not allowed into the hospital. He has not seen them since.

Much later in the pandemic we will learn that patients with severe oxygen deficits somehow do not *feel* short of breath. In some strange, diabolical way, the virus suppresses the feeling of suffocation that normally occurs when the blood oxygen level is low from a bilateral pneumonia.

The researchers think it has to do with Covid's unique way of attacking the lungs. The virus triggers an inflammatory response, but it's a response that mainly blocks oxygen from diffusing across the lung membrane to the blood. The Covid syndrome does *not* seem to prevent the carbon dioxide from diffusing out of the blood and into the lungs.

Since their carbon dioxide level doesn't build up and up in the blood stream the patient doesn't feel all that short of breath.

Diabolical.

Because the patient *looks* comfortable, the ER doctors have been sending these patients with minimal symptoms home when they should be admitting and treating them. The physicians don't realize the patient is actually critically ill, they just don't present with the classic complaints.

The ER nurse asks me to send her warmest wishes to Mr. B., and I hurry up to my unit.

In the ICU, we put on the three layers of protective clothing, don the respirator masks and face shields, pull on gloves and step into the unit. In morning report, I learn that Mr. B. has become unresponsive; blood clots to the brain, the ICU Attending is sure. It's the "Black Mamba snake" clotting disorder. The patient exhibits no gag reflex when the suction catheter is pushed down his airway. He was weaned off his sedation...with no effect.

In normal times, the nurse lightens the ventilated patient's sedation once a day to assess the brain function. Can the patient move all limbs, nod or shake the head to a question, understand where he is? With the frequent shortages of sedation and anesthetics, the patients have been waking up without warning. Panic drives them to reach for their breathing tube. I am grateful that lately, the medication supplies have been adequate.

Dr. C, the British Anesthesiologist that we all like so much, was on call during the night. He reports to the Critical Care team. He has a classic dry British wit. Lately there has been no place for humor.

"I put in a consult for Palliative Care," Dr. C tells the Attending. "Should be here mid-morning." He reports that the dialysis catheter in the patient's groin clotted. Again. He replaced it.

I ask why don't the anticoagulants we have been infusing stop the blood from clotting? The resident replies that they still have no idea which of the clotting mechanisms the virus is triggering, so they're not sure what therapy would be best.

"We're shooting in the bloody dark," he say bitterly, without apologizing for the pun.

As the physicians begin their rounds, the housekeeper, Mrs. Y., asks them to not step on the wet floor she just mopped. I lift my mask for a second and breathe in the smell of bleach. It tingles my nose. The bleach is a welcome scent, it is killing the virus on hard surfaces. As I don a 4th layer of protective clothing before going into the patient's room, I greet her. Mrs. Y. silently nods in reply and continues mopping.

I go in to assess my first patient, Mrs. W., a woman in her late 50's who works in our hospital on the OB-GYN floor. She is stable on high doses of intravenous epinephrine (adrenalin), given to support the blood pressure. The blood gas, though, is horribly low, even with the ventilator sending 100% oxygen to the lungs. The Respiratory Therapist, a short woman with gray dreadlocks and a lovely face beneath her mask and face shield, increases the positive pressure on the ventilator. I pray the high pressure will not rupture the lungs.

Finished with assessing Mrs. W., I go to Mr. B.'s room. I check his intravenous drips, which are outside the room, delivering fluids and medications through long extension tubing. Somebody has stuck a sticker with a smiley face like an emoji on the bag of dextrose and sodium. Someone in Stores, maybe. It brings a little smile to my lips.

I prepare to enter Mr. B's room just as Dr. P., the Palliative Care doctor, arrives. He is a tall, lean, soft spoken man with thinning hair and the gentlest of manners. I have heard he studied to be a priest before choosing medicine.

I would be glad to give him my confession.

In Mr. B.'s little room, the Palliative Care doctor tests the patient's reflexes. The pupils are fixed and dilated, as they are on a corpse. There is no blink response to a sterile gauze pad rubbed across the opened eyes. A jab to the chest with the sharp end of a broken wooden Q-tip elicits no pain response.

Leaving the room, the Palliative Care doctor makes a note in the electronic chart. He writes that the patient is "brain Dead," which means he is legally dead. That gives the hospital the right to stop all treatments. He recommends asking the family for permission to turn off the ventilator.

After checking with the Critical Care team, I call the family and ask someone to come to the ICU. This is a change in policy. Up until now, family members were not allowed into the hospital. But too many patients have died without a loved one at their side, so the policy was amended: one family member may visit the dead or dying.

An hour later Mr. B.'s son arrives. The Palliative Care physician is paged and arrives promptly. The doctor explains how the patient failed the brain death protocol and is legally dead. The son, a man in his early twenties who resembles his dad, says he understands. I know he is putting on a brave face.

I lead the son into the room once he's donned the gloves, mask and gown. He bends down to kiss his dad on the forehead through the mask. Dr. P. and I wait silently by the door.

"Can you do one thing for me?" the son asks.

Dr. P steps closer to listen.

"I understand, you're going to take him off the breathing machine. If...if he does take a breath, I want you to put him back on the machine. Okay?"

"Of course."

Dr. P. disconnects the ventilator tubing and turns off the machine. He also cancels the alarm. As the three of us stand and watch, staring at the patient's chest, we hear a ventilator alarm going off. I look at Dr. P., puzzled.

Nurse O sticks her head into the room. "Your other patient is coding. We have another code in room one, can you come?"

Seeing that Dr. P. is staying with the son, I hurriedly shed my outer layer and pull on a second isolation gown, stored in a trash bag outside the other room. I run into Mrs. W.'s room, where a medical student and a resident are administering CPR. I grab an amp of adrenalin from the red crash cart and inject it into the patient's IV, already running full bore to try and bring up her blood pressure.

Mrs. W. survives the code, but she, too, is now without reflexes. I don't know how much more she can tolerate. Nurse O comes in and helps me clean up the room, which is strewn with discarded instruments, empty packaging and linen.

After Mr. B.'s body, cleaned and wrapped in a body bag, is sent to the temporary morgue out in the parking lot, a special cleaner comes in and sprays the entire room with a powerful disinfectant. Once it has had time to penetrate the virus that covers everything, I ask the housekeeper to clean the room.

Mrs. Y., the housekeeper, dons her gown and pushes her rolling bucket into the room. She sees that the mattress is still deformed where Mr. B. had lain unmoving for eight days. At the sight of the empty bed, she breaks into tears and steps out of the room.

"It is too much. It is too much, the dying," she says, tears wetting her mask. She is petite, with lovely hazel eyes that look green in a certain light. Her speech has the soft accent of her native Peru. Mrs. Y. came to the US with a degree, a child and a husband. Since her degree was not recognized, she took the housekeeping work and is taking college classes.

As the housekeeper looks around the ICU, she sees all the nurses are looking into large, black plastic bags. "What is that?" she asks me. I am standing at the nursing station holding my own black bag.

"It's from the Red Cross," I tell her. "They sent gifts for all of us. We got cologne and powder, hand sanitizer and a whole lot of stuff."

About to return to the empty room to clean it, Mrs. Y. spots the Housekeeping Supervisor walking toward her carrying one of the big black plastic bags. She offers it to Mrs. Y.

"For me?" the housekeeper asks.

"For you."

I approach her and gently say. "Come on, let's go see what they gave us."

Mrs. Y. and I walk to the nursing lounge, where Nurse O is already looking over her booty.

Mrs. Y. sits down and with timid hands opens her bag. She begins to cry once more. "I am so grateful, they thought of me. They brought a gift for *me*."

I look over at my colleague, who is also crying. We open our bottles of cologne and spray ourselves. It is like a girl's night out.

Although the cologne will not kill the virus, it does transform tears of sorrow to tears of joy.

After the shift is over, Nurse O and I ride to the hotel. As we enter the lobby, we see a group of Texas firefighters. They are seated at a long, out-door table, eating and drinking and swapping stories. All the firemen follow Nurse O with their eyes, she is such a lovely woman.

Nurse O and I exchange text messages from our hotel rooms as we clean up and change our clothes, nobody has a roommate. When we go down to grab a quick meal, I whisper to my friend, "Don't say anything, but my kids are coming to the hotel."

"Say, *what?* Are you crazy?"

I know it's against the rules, but they have been begging to see where I have been staying. To be honest, they have been growing stir crazy stuck at home, so my husband and I gave in and said they could just peak in and see where mama has been living most of the time. Since early March!

I tiptoe to the front entrance of the hotel and gesture to my husband in the car. He unlocks the door and lets the two young ones run to me (I've showered and shampooed *twice* just for this occasion). We walk past the table of Texas firefighters. The red fire truck that the New York City fire department loaned them is parked outside, making the hotel a temporary fire house.

One of the men sees that my son is wearing a New York Yankees baseball cap. The man winks and says to him, "Who's got the best baseball team this year (even though they aren't playing games yet).

"Yankees, of course," replies my boy, who is all of eight years old. He has seen the video tapes and the reports on ESPN how the Houston Astros had cheated in the past and didn't deserve their title.

"I don't think so," says the fireman from Texas. "I think we got the better team this year."

As we step into the elevator and the doors begin to close, my son yells out, "Astros SUCK!"

Hoots of laughter ring out from the men at the table, but it's all in good humor, they have come to know and respect us nurses, as we have come to know and admire these volunteers who traveled so far to help out the NY Fire Department, which has suffered so many losses to the Covid virus.

Riding the elevator, I'm embarrassed and proud and happy, and for just a moment, I'm not exhausted or discouraged.

It's a small miracle in a time of tragedy.

THE HOME REMEDY

May 12, 2020

Although it is mid-week in the ICU, the weekdays and weekends are all the same. Every day there are shortages of staff, equipment and medications. A few more traveling nurses have been brought in to supplement the staff. They are mostly excellent; highly professional and experienced, and the regular staff are grateful to have them. The young ones are undergoing baptism by fire, but they keep on coming back. Even Nurse Y is growing in confidence.

When I ask the night nurse, a traveling nurse from Wisconsin, how was her night, the newcomer reports she had an empty bed for the last four hours of her shift.

"*Four* hours? *Empty?* Aren't you the lucky one?"

The hospital census has dropped from its peak of over 400 to 104, but in the ICU, no bed stays empty for long. After seven to ten days on the ward, many of the Covid-19 patients develop a heart attack or stroke, or sink into septic shock and multi-organ failure. They are likely to make the ICU their final port of call.

As if the ravages that the virus inflicts on the body aren't bad enough, now patients are suffering from the effects of their treatments as well. Some are prescribed by a physician, others are home remedies.

A number of the Emergency Room doctors are still treating Covid-19 patients with the antibiotic Zithromax and the anti-malaria drug touted by the right-wing media, Chloroquine, we don't understand why. Mr G transferred to the ICU during the night with an abnormal EKG and slow heart rate caused by the controversial drug. He has a temporary pacemaker that is threaded through a catheter in his neck.

Before I have time to complete my first patient assessment, Mr G's heart rate drops dangerously low. I alert the ICU team and page the Cardiology Service, STAT ("Life or death"). The two teams are soon pouring over the EKG and puzzling over the slow pulse (bradycardia), which the pacemaker is supposed to prevent.

"Maybe the wire is coiled in the heart," I suggest as I adjust the intravenous pump.

The senior Cardiologist is surprised. "I didn't think the ICU nurses knew so much about pacemakers," he says.

"Bed two, three and seven are all cardiac patients," I explain. "We get so many heart patients because of the fricking chloroquinoline, it's like working in a CCU around here."

The ICU Attending orders a STAT portable chest x-ray. Sure enough, the wire is coiled in the heart chamber, preventing it from establishing a good interface with the muscle. As both teams watch the heart monitor above the bed, the Cardiologist pulls the wire back and gently advances it, fishing for a "bite." Finally, the tip of the catheter establishes a good contact and the heart rate comes up to 72, the rate set on the pacemaker.

As the heart doctors leave the unit, the ICU Fellow winks at me. He knows a good nurse when he finds one.

Minutes later, the ward clerk calls out. "ER on the line, we have an admission!"

With a weary sigh, I wash my hands, dry them and pick up the phone to take report. Even with my two months of battle field experience, I am still shocked at what I hear.

Mr. L arrived at the ER unconscious. The EMT told the physician that the man's roommate reported the patient had shown signs of the Covid infection. He was depressed and swallowed a bottle of household cleaning solution to fight off the virus. The EMT brought the bottle with him so the doctors could assess the damage. The fluid contained bleach, a powerful corrosive.

In the ER, the GI consultant examined the patient's esophagus with a flexible fiberoptic scope. The lining of the esophagus was red and eroded. The man would not be able to swallow even liquids for a long time. He might even need a long section of the esophagus surgically removed, since a perforation of the eroded esophagus would leak bacteria and fungi into the chest, a catastrophic event for any patient, let alone a Covid-19 one.

Hanging up the phone, I want to go out into the street and yell and scream at the right-wing pundits who have pushed dangerous, even lethal home remedies, like swallowing cleaning fluid. Some critics asked if those pundits held stock in the company that manufactured the medication, which triggered a lot of ranting and finger pointing among them. They sure didn't produce a record of their investment portfolio for the public to see.

When the patient arrives in the ICU, I settle him into the bed while the Respiratory Therapist adjusts the ventilator. The patient is a thirty-year old construction worker. He is stocky and muscular and has strong, calloused hands and a baby face.

The ICU team look at the photos of the damaged esophagus attached to the chart. They are shocked and appalled. I am relieved that the patient is unconscious, the pain would have been unbearable were he awake.

"What are you going to order for Mr. L's Covid?" I ask. The ICU Attending is not sure, no one has found an effective treatment yet. "I guess, Zithro and Chloroquinoline. And convalescent antibodies."

"But all our patients in the unit are *dying!*"

I am so upset, the ER physician and the medical doctors on the wards are not trying new treatments, even though the drugs they are ordering are clearly failing the patients. I downloaded Covid treatment protocols from hospitals in Dubai, in Boston, in China. Hospitals are trying many different treatment protocols, searching for something that will kill this virus.

A year ago I mentored a nursing student who was born in Wuhan, China. The nurse returned to China at the first news of the outbreak. She has kept me informed of their failures and successes there. The even sent me pictures of herself and a co-worker, they were dressed in full hazmat protective gear. We reuse our N95 masks and plastic isolation gowns all shift long.

"What about Interferon?" I ask the ICU Attending. "What about the HIV cocktail? What about suppressing the cytokine storm (the body's sometimes hyper-reactive immune response) with high dose steroids? What about..."

The Attending promises to talk to the Infectious Disease Fellow and explore their options. Although Mr. L is not expected to survive, given his horrific injuries from the cleaning solution, nobody is giving up on him.

During a late lunch, I try to reach a family member by phone, I need to determine who is the next of kin with the power to make decisions. The family is scattered all over the US. Reaching a brother in Los Angeles, I send him a photograph of my patient via text messaging. He confirms it is his brother in the ICU.

"Please, please help him," the brother says, crying. "He is a good man. He never hurt anyone. Please help him."

I cannot in good conscience give the brother false expectations. At the same time, I do not want to take away all hope.

"The virus causes a very bad infection, you know that, right?" I say. He replies he understands. "We are doing everything we can, the doctors are doing their best. I just want you to know, your brother is in critical condition. He is very sick."

The brother understands. "Pray for L., won't you nurse? I know you have many patients, but say a prayer for him."

I promise, even though I no longer believe in miracles. I say good-bye and hang up.

With all of the drugs and ventilators and pacemakers in the world, I know with infinite sadness that they are no match for the right-wing mouthpieces, including the White House administration, who push dangerous, ineffec-tive treatments, like swallowing cleaning fluid. They never see the consequences of their igno-rant home remedies. Only the pathologist in the morgue and the hospital staff see it and have to explain the end results to the family.

The conservatives who hawk their snake oil cures are a plague on the world. I want to know why no one has come up with a treatment pro-tocol that silences them, so my patients at least have a *chance* to survive.

Later in the shift I spot Miss Q, the petite Pharm-D. She is talking with the ICU team in their on-call room. I step in to listen. As soon as I get a chance I ask if they will be giving Remdesivir to Mr. L. Miss Q looks sad for a moment. In a low voice, almost a whisper, she tells me that the hospital has asked the pharmaceutical company to take part in the Remdesivir drug trials the company is sponsoring. It's the only way to get the drug.

"We'll get it, won't we?" I ask.

She shakes her head "No. Every one of our requests to the pharmaceutical company was denied. Our pharmacy director doesn't understand it. Neither does the Infectious Disease Chief or the Chief Medical Officer."

I leave the room infuriated. Why won't some Fortune 500 company sign us up for drug trials? Are our patients not *good* enough? Are their Medicare and Medicaid plans not *rich* enough? Other New York hospitals are using the drug, which seems to have the best chance of beating back the virus.

When Nurse O sees the anger and sorrow in my eyes, she knows to give me space.

I promise to tell her on the phone when we are in our hotel rooms what I learned in the on-call room, even though I know it will get us both crying our eyes out.

POST-COVID SYNDROME

June 7, 2020

Now that New York has reduced our daily infection rates to a low number (we "flattened the curve") and admissions for Covid infection are way down, you might think we would be on easy street in the hospital. Sadly, that's not the case. Instead, we are seeing patients who have survived the virus, but they have serious, severe chronic conditions now that are almost as life-threatening as the original infection.

I am worried about these "long haulers" who look like they had previous Covid infection. After they recover, they come back in as post infection complications, but we don't know when or if they will re-infect again. Can we trust they are not spreading the virus if their nasal swab comes back negative? Or will they always test positive? It seems like the test result depends on their immune system. The virus can really knock out the immune response: does that mean they will spread the virus?

This is what worries me when Mr. U. is admitted.

Mr. U. is a 27-year old bus operator. He is an HIV patient who has been on anti-viral medications for two years. He believes he had the Covid infection two or three weeks ago, but was never tested. Now he's come to our hospital with nagging cough and chest pains. In the ER, the deep nasal swab came back negative for the virus, but they did not test for Covid antibodies, I'm not sure why. They aren't treating him for Covid infection, either.

I ask the ICU Resident, who is writing the admitting orders in the patient's electronic chart, "If Mr. U. is coming in with Covid *symptoms* and an x-ray that is *classic* for Covid, plus he has multiple blood clots in the lung and in the heart, why aren't you treating him for Covid Syndrome? Why isn't he even on isolation precautions? Covid patients are still shedding the virus for up to 90 days? Aren't they?"

The Resident says they don't have any test results that prove it's a Covid case, all his tests have been negative so far. I tell the Resident, "You *have* to test for antibodies." He replies that the antibody test takes a week to come back, he doesn't see the value in it.

Dr. K, the Infectious Disease Attending, comes in with his team. They gather with the ICU team outside the patient's room. I repeat my questions to Dr. K and finish by asking if Mr. L could be a super-spreader, given his weakened immune system.

Dr. K crosses his arms and looks up at the ceiling. He says, "I saw the x-rays from the night before. And the ones from this morning. He does have a broken glass pattern all over the lung fields."

I wait for him to continue.

"He's on anti-viral meds at home for his HIV. It's possible they are suppressing viral loads in the naso-pharynx. That could give a negative swab."

"Uh-huh," I say. "So, shouldn't he be on isolation, just to be safe?"

Now the ICU Resident is getting nervous. He could have made the same observations that I made. Dr. K recommends they treat the patient for Covid, despite the negative nasal swab, and tht they test for antibodies, even though the chronic HIV disease might make it difficult for the patient's immune system to even mount a good response.

After the ID team leaves, the ICU resident adds Airborne Precautions to the admitting orders. And he puts the patient on the Covid treatment protocol, although we still haven't been given Remdesivir.

A LULL IN BATTLE

July 2, 2020

July has finally come and we are in a lull. Work in the ICU looks like it has gone back to normal, but of course, it hasn't. Like malignant hypertension (the silent killer that slowly destroys the kidneys), the damage wrought by the pandemic is still present, eating away at our hearts. At our souls. Because *we* are not the same. We will *never be* the same. How could we be, when our hearts have been squeezed until they burst? How could we be when our eyes have cried and cried until we have no more tears? When our bodies have become numb from the fatigue, and our hopes have been suffocated by so much loss? So much death?

How can we do the same work again when our nerves are shattered to the point that we can't sleep, we can't eat, we fight with our family and we have lost the love for our patients that sustained us for years and year and years?

The Fall promises to be another challenge, perhaps as great as the one we faced this past Spring. Perhaps greater. We will likely see seasonal flu bringing waves of patients in through the ER and the clinics. We will see more Covid-19 patients. And we will see our staff hollowed out by illness, fatigue, despair and death.

Do you really expect me to march back into battle and face the same enemy when my hospital is no more prepared for war now than it was in February and March? The oxygen ports in the wards and in the step-down units have not been upgraded to a high flow system, so once again we won't be able to hook up ventilators there and support our patients who suffer from pneumonia and septic shock. We will have to rely on the big green oxygen tanks, which run empty and then..."Attention! Attention! Code Blue in room..."

The ICU doesn't have negative pressure fans in all the rooms to blow airborne pathogens like Covid-19 out into the free-flowing wind, where they will be safely dispersed. And don't tell me that influenza patients only require "Droplet Precautions." "Droplet precautions" is nothing more than a simple room with a door that's closed. *No.* I want to be protected by a negative pressure or a HEPA filter that removes the viral particles when the patient coughs or receives a breathing treatment, so that the pathogens won't settle in my hair and on my arms and my clothes and my stethoscope. I want to be *safe*. Really, truly safe.

The hospital hasn't provided us with enough personal protective equipment so that we won't have to reuse them for twelve long hours. And

I'm sure there's no big stockpile of critical medications we will need if we face another avalanche of intubated and unstable patients.

Of course, the hospital doesn't have the money that we need to make those and other improvements. It is not a profitable private hospital with wealthy donors and high-paying patients. Our reimbursement rates are criminally low. The Federal government and the private insurers reimburse the Ritchie Rich hospitals at a rate that is up to three times higher for the same procedures we perform. Medicare and Medicaid don't pay enough to pay the bills, so where will the money come from for capital improvements or stockpiling supplies? *My* hospital can barely pay the wages and the expenses under normal times. In a crisis, we are stripped bare.

I don't want to gear up again with my four layers of clothing until I know that Central Stores has all of the best PPE's on the market to protect us – and our families – against whatever pathogen is invading our facility full blast.

I don't want to go through those Emergency Room doors every morning if New York State has not increased its financial support for poverty hospitals like mine big, BIG time, so that the institution can hire extra staff when we need it most, like traveling nurses, extra housekeepers, extra lab technicians and extra morgue attendants.

I don't want to care for our patients – largely poor and people of color, many of them immigrants hoping for a better life – when the big pharmaceutical companies are *refusing* to enroll us in drug studies and give us the most promising treatments in their arsenal.

And I most definitely don't want to go through hell again, risking my life and the lives of my family, until the Federal Government raises its Medicare and Medicaid payments to a reasonable rate that will sustain and allow improvements that we so desperately need, and until it gives out-and-out grants for structural improvements, like upgrading the oxygen delivery systems.

Then I will gladly tie up my hair, hang my stethoscope around my neck, tuck my nursing shears in my pocket, clip my watch to my uniform and march with my fellow hospital workers back into battle, because that's the deal I signed up for. That's the oath I swore as a nurse.

That's the love I have for my patients and my co-workers.

I'm ready to go...will you have my back?

LOOKING AHEAD

August 15, 2020

We're well into our summer, and the hospital has allowed some of us to take vacation. Not that we can travel very far. My family went camping in the Adirondacks. It was buggy and hot and we had a fair amount of rain (the tent leaked!), but it was away from everyone and everything. That was the best part.

My husband was anxious to try out this solar oven he bought. It actually did pretty good, although I missed the taste of a really charred burger. Boys and their toys...

Going to work, Nurse O no longer cries when she sees the hospital building as it comes into sight. The hospital provided us with free psychological counseling by telephone. At first, I didn't think I'd get much benefit from the sessions, but they did help a lot of us. There were a couple of sessions where some nurses really ripped into the administration. I think the venting helped all of us.

Nurse O is sleeping a whole lot better, and I'm back to sleeping with my husband, he doesn't have to sleep on a cot in the basement anymore. I kind of wish the kids were little ones again and I could invite them to come sleep with us, but it's okay, at least I can sit with them as they get sleepy and kiss them good-night. The simple joys of a mother at home.

I'm back to doing the laundry, too. Some things never change!

As the new school year approaches, I'm worried that the teachers aren't prepared for the virus. Is it in their training to teach in a pandemic? How can we support our educators to put aside their fears and focus on the innocent vulnerable children. How can we protect them *and* our teachers? I can't see little children wearing the P100 elastometric masks, they scare everyone.

Will there be enough workers to clean the classrooms? No one signed up to this. As Nurses, it's our oath to treat the sick, whatever the danger. But for teachers, keeping everyone safe from this *highly* infectious disease is not in their training. It's no wonder they are scared to death.

Just before the pandemic came down hard on us in New York I had bid on a nursing position with a research company. Twenty-plus years in the ICU is enough, thank you very much. The company rep liked my resume and the online interview went well, I thought, but with the pandemic they are postponing any projects until next year. So I guess I'll stay in the ICU.

At least we're back to an assignment that lets us properly care for our patients: two per nurse. After our Spring endurance test of three or four patients for one nurse, and at least two of them unstable, the regular assignment is a pleasure. Yesterday toward the end of my shift I gave a patient a back rub. That doesn't sound like much, but I missed the intimate connection nurses strive for, giving that extra touch and talking with the patient.

There is one more piece of good news. Flu season looks less scary than what we thought it would be back in early Spring. New Yorkers are the best! We've been following social distancing and wearing masks in public, for the most part, and the Governor and Mayor have been very cautious about opening up businesses that could give Covid the environment that spreads the disease.

Dr. K, the ID Attending, says he wouldn't be surprised if flu season was significantly milder than the last few years. If New Yorkers continue taking precaution and respecting the public health guidelines, the influenza virus won't have the usual vectors for spreading through the community. People have to just keep the faith and keep their distance, like, in the movie theaters that are about to open. And the gyms and the libraries.

The library! I'll be able to take my children to the library next month, more evidence we have done more than "flatten the curve; we have decimated it.

Come on, America, get your act together. If we can hang tough, follow instructions and listen to the public health professionals, you can, too. You better not be coming to Times Square and shedding virus all up and down Broadway. No, way. Follow the science and flatten your curve, we'll all be better off.

I asked Nurse O as we rode home last night if she was bitter. She said no, she wasn't bitter exactly, she was tired. Tired of the shortages and the outdated equipment. Tired of the politicians protesting they can't afford to raise our reimbursement rates. Tired of the government – city, state and federal – funneling resources to the gold-plated medical centers in Manhattan. "Why can't our patients get the same level of care?" she asked. "They hurt just as bad. When they die, their family mourns just as much."

I remember reading somewhere how New York had a tax on stock transfers for like *decades,* until Governor Pataki eliminated it. There's a big pool of money there that could build us a brand new state of the art hospital, but the political leaders won't make it happen.

They don't care about our patients: poor people of color, many of them immigrants.

But *we* care. That's why we came in to work every day and did battle with that terrible virus. That's why Nurse O rode in the car with me, broke into tears at the sight of the facility, took the time to calm herself, and then marched right back in with me.

The hospital has promised to hold a memorial for our co-workers who passed on. There are a lot of them, their pictures were posted in the hospital newsletter. I recognized every face. I could even hear their voices. I'm going to attend, come Hell or high water. I'm going to remember them all my life. I hope to God our tears water the seeds of a better health care system.

When our voices at the service ring up to Heaven, I hope they are heard all the way to Albany and Washington, DC.

HEALING MEDITATIONS FOR CAREGIVERS

MEDITATIONS FOR CAREGIVERS

Use these next pages to write about your thoughts, your feeling, your hopes and your dreams. These are for your personal use; take the time to open your heart and let your emotions express themselves.

Remember that it's not your fault if you feel sad or depressed. You are going through PTSD; it is a normal process. Healing takes time, so give yourself all of the time that you need.

Feel proud that you put yourself on the front lines of battle and did your part to heal...to comfort...to honor the ones who have fallen.

With love and gratitude,
Nurse T and Timothy Sheard

BREATHING TO CENTER YOUR SOUL

Even before you reflect on your experience in the hospital, nursing home or home-care service, it will be helpful to practice this simple breathing exercise. The exercises will help you collect your thoughts and sort out your memories.

Assume a comfortable position in a quiet space (you can even be at work), and try the breathing exercise. Don't worry if you are not "doing it right." As long as you feel yourself beginning to relax, you are mastering the exercise perfectly...because you are perfect just the way you are.

Begin each of the meditations that follow with this breathing exercise, and use it at work or wherever you are to become more centered and at peace. Repeat this exercise for a full minute, or until you feel your body and mind beginning to relax.

Let thoughts flit by and disappear

Be in the moment. Just be yourself.

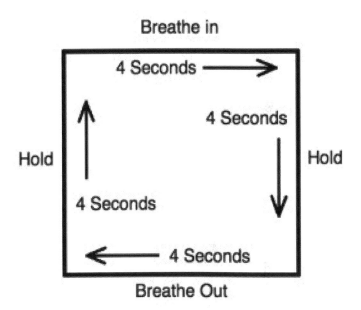

HEALING YOURSELF

Begin by reminding yourself that you are a caring and loving person – a *Caregiver*.

Your goal is to treat yourself with the same tender loving care that you give to your patients/clients. That is the healing pathway; that is how you regain your joy and love of your craft. This is how you find peace in your heart.

MEDITATION

Begin with the breathing exercise. Then...

Place your palm over your heart.

Feel your sweetly beating heart. It is a loving heart. A giving heart. Give that love to yourself.

Wrap your arms around yourself and hug yourself. You are loved by so many, never forget to love yourself as well.

WRITINGEXERCISE–HEALINGYOURSELF

Begin writing below with the words: "I care about..." Then write about the individuals you care about – your family, your co-workers, friends, patients and patient families. Picture them looking at you and thanking you for your care. You are modest in your reply, and grateful for the opportunity to comfort them.

After writing about others, imagine *you* being the recipient of that much caring. Write what the ones who received your care might say to you to express their affection and respect for you. Let *yourself* be loved and cherished with their words, for you deserve all of their love.

_____

_____

_____

_____

_____

_____

_____

WRITING EXERCISE – HEALING YOURSELF
(Continued)

_____

_____

_____

_____

_____

_____

_____

_____

_____

_____

_____

_____

_____

_____

YOUR COMMON HUMANITY

You and your co-workers are members of a great and noble family; the family of care-givers. Many years ago, nurses were known as "Medical Sisters." Theirs was a religious calling; a life dedicated to serving the sick and the poor. Take pride and find strength in your membership of this ancient and honorable family.

MEDITATION

Begin with the breathing exercise. Then...

Imagine a family gathering, like you might see at Thanksgiving or some other holiday. In your mind, invite all of the family members that you cherish and enjoy. Remember that your "family" goes beyond ties of marriage and birth, it includes your co-workers and friends.

Now, imagine your favorite patients and their families joining you. Listen as they toast you and tell stories of their time with you. Feel their gratitude and love, for you have earned it.

WRITING EXERCISE
– YOUR COMMON HUMANITY

Write a Thank You letter to a co-worker who helped you when you needed it most, when you were going through a difficult time. Do you think that colleague ever went through the same sort of trials and was helped by someone just like you?

Then, write another Thank You letter to a patient or family for the opportunity you enjoyed to care for them, to get to know them, and to comfort them.

_____

_____

_____

_____

_____

_____

_____

_____

WRITING EXERCISE – YOUR COMMON HUMANITY (Continued)

_____

_____

_____

_____

_____

_____

_____

_____

_____

_____

_____

_____

_____

VANQUISHING PAINFUL FEELINGS

Many Caregivers are troubled by feelings of guilt, sorrow, or loneliness. Often, we have looked back with regret at a path we chose or an outcome we wished had not come about.

It is easy and all too common to berate ourselves for what we think we failed to do. This harsh self-judgement is wrong. First, it is wrong because nobody is perfect. "To err is human." Holding yourself up to a standard or perfection is unrealistic and only leads to a sense of failure.

Second, this self-judgement does not reflect the totality of your life's work. You have taken countless actions to help one in need. Your heart has always been in the right place, even if at times you stumbled or fell short in some small way.

We need not be perfect. We need not be always correct or successful. We need only to try our best and learn from our mistakes.

MEDITATION

Begin with the breathing exercise. Then...

Consider a moment when you did not achieve the goal you set for yourself.

Now, look at your face...your arms...your hands and legs. Does a blemish here, a dark spot or a scar there make us any less beautiful? Any less your wonderful self? Say to yourself, "I am imperfect, but I am perfect in my own way."

WRITING EXERCISE – GUILT

Imagine that the guilt that you feel is imbedded in an old leather jacket that you are wearing. The leather is cracked and faded. It is worn out.

Now, imagine slowly pealing off the old leather jacket. As youuun button the jacket and peel it off, you peel off the feelings of doubt and guilt and regret.

What do you find beneath? Describe the colors and fabrics of your life. Then write about how you will walk and skip and dance in sunlight and in moonlight as you show off your lovely clothes...your lovely self.

_____

_____

_____

_____

_____

_____

_____

WRITING EXERCISE – GUILT (Continued)

_____

_____

_____

_____

_____

_____

_____

_____

_____

_____

_____

_____

_____

MEDITATION ON SORROW

Begin with the breathing exercise. Then...

For any patient, co-worker, family member or friend you have lost, imagine them in their happiest moments, laughing with you... embracing you... loving you. Raise a glass, imaginary or real, to their memory and to their life. Be grateful you were able to share some time with them, however brief, however fleeting, for you were a part of their life, and they were grateful to you for being part of theirs.

Because some, or perhaps, many of the sick that you cared for died, you naturally feel a deep sorrow at the loss. Perhaps you led the family into the room to say good-bye to their loved one. Or perhaps you said good-bye for them, as they were not allowed into your facility.

WRITING EXERISE – SORROW

Sorrow is a normal response to loss. But it is not the *only* response. In any time of mourning, there are family and friends who will celebrate the life that was lived to the full. There will be humorous stories of past escapades. Toasts to past victories and accomplishments. Memories of time together, celebrated again and again.

It is important to remember the life that was lived as much as the life that was lost.

Imagine you are at a gathering of family, friends or co-workers, and write a toast to the person that you lost. Add a humorous anecdote if you can recall one.

_____

_____

_____

_____

_____

_____

_____

_____

_____

_____

_____

_____

MEDITATION ON LONELINESS

Perhaps you sequestered in a hotel room not far from your hospital, cut off from your home. Or perhaps you can go home, but there you stay apart to protect your family from possible exposure to the virus.

This isolation can lead to deep, powerful feelings of loneliness and despair. This is a common experience that many caregivers go through it. You are not alone in your sorrow, although you *feel* alone.

Imagine a talk between you and someone you love. Listen to the words that the beloved shares with you.

Now imagine that same beloved person is imagining a similar conversation with you. What are you saying to him or her? What are you hearing? You are never really disconnected from the people you love, you only have temporary loss of the link – the video chat program. Believe in the connection.

WRITING EXERCISE – LONELINESS

Begin writing with these words: "I am by myself right now, but I am not alone." Then write the words you would like to share with family or friends, were they with you in this moment.

Next, write their words in response to you.

After writing their words, read them aloud to yourself, as they would read to you, and feel the love they have for you.

_____

_____

_____

_____

_____

_____

_____

_____

_____

_____

MEDITATION ON ANGER

Of *course* you are angry. You are angry at the virus for ravaging your community. Your whole world. You are angry at the failure of the government to implement and enforce strong, effective public health measures that would have stopped the virus from spreading as soon as the first cases were identified.

Anger without action can turn into anger turned within. That leads to despair.

Taking action means harnessing the energy of your feelings for a constructive purpose that will make a difference in the community where you live and where your patients and family and friends have suffered.

Imagine the individuals in power who have failed to exercise their duty to protect the public (and you) from the pandemic. As the anger towards them rises, think about what you, your co-workers and friends can do to replace those failed leaders. Think, also, how you can take part in remedial work now in your community and your country.

Turn the anger toward failed individuals to a commitment to make the world a more just and healthful place.

WRITING EXERCISE – ANGER

Write a letter to an official who is in a position to implement real public health measures for your community. Share your letter with friends and co-workers and ask them if they would write letters, too.

Take part in political associations that call for social justice, public health and equality for all.

_____

_____

_____

_____

_____

_____

_____

_____

_____

_____

_____

ABOUT THE AUTHORS

Nurse T is a veteran critical care nurse. She has more than twenty years of hospital duty in her resume and has mentored scores of young nurses. Nurse T was born and raised in New York City, where she and her husband are raising three delightful, savvy children.

This book is dedicated to my beloved husband and children, who inspired and supported me through this challenging time, and to my colleagues – nurses and doctors working in an unimaginable pandemic – who were relentless and tireless as we worked together. I would work with all of you – in any pandemic – any time.

Timothy Sheard, RN (retired), has worked in hospitals for over 40 years. He is a long-time advocate for labor unions and social justice. Timothy is the author of nine medical mystery novels and founder of Hard Ball Press, a social justice imprint.

Titles From Hard Ball Press

A Great Vision – A Militant Family's Journey Through the Twentieth Century – by Richard March

Caring – 1199 Nursing Home Workers Tell Their Story

Fight For Your Long Day – Classroom Edition, by Alex Kudera

Good Trouble: A Shoeleather History of Nonviolent Direct Action, Steve Thornton

I Just Got Elected, Now What? The New Union Officer's Handbook, Bill Barry

I Still Can't Fly: Confessions of a Lifelong Troublemaker, Kevin John Carroll

Legacy Costs: The Story of a Factory Town, Richard Hudelson

Love Dies, a thriller, by Timothy Sheard

The Man Who Fell From the Sky, Bill Fletcher, Jr.

Murder of a Post Office Manager, A Legal Thriller, by Paul Felton

New York Hustle – Pool Rooms, School Rooms and Street Corners, a memoir, Stan Maron

The Secrets of the Snow, a book of p0etry, Hiva Panahi

Sixteen Tons, a Novel, by Kevin Corley

The Union Member's Complete Guide, Michael Mauer

Throw Out the Water, a novel, by Kevin Corley

What Did You Learn at Work Today?, by Helena Worthen

Welcome to the Union, by Michael Mauer

Wining Richmond, Gayle McLaughlin

With Our Loving Hands, 1199 Nursing Home Workers Tell Their Story, Steve Bender, Ed.

Woman Missing, A Mill Town Mystery, by Linda Nordquist

THE LENNY MOSS MYSTERIES by Timothy Sheard

This Won't Hurt A Bit
Some Cuts Never Heal

A Race Against Death
No Place To Be Sick
Slim To None
A Bitter Pill
Someone Has To Die
One Foot in the Grave
All Bleeding Stops Eventually

CHILDREN'S BOOKS

The Cabbage That Came Back, Stephen Pearl (author), Rafael Pearl (Illustrator), Sara Pearl (translator)

Down on James Street (coming Winter 2020-2021), by Nicole McCandless, illustrations by Byron Gramby (coming Winter 2020-2021)

Freedom Soldiers, (a YA novel) by Katherine Williams

Good Guy Jake, Mark Torres (author), Yana Podrieez (Illustrator), Madelin Arroyo (translator)

Hats Off For Gabbie, Marivir Montebon (author), Yana Podriez (illustrator), Madelin Arroyo (translator)

Jimmy's Carwash Adventure, Victor Narro (author & translator), Yana Podriez (illustrator)

Joelito's Big Decision, Ann Berlak (author), Daniel Camacho (Illustrator), José Antonio Galloso (Translator)

Journey to Para Todos, By Alejandra Domenzain, Spanish translation by Irene Prieto de Coogan, Illustrations by Katherine Loh

Manny & The Mango Tree, Ali R. Bustamante (author), Monica Lunot-Kuker (illustrator), Mauricio Niebla (translator)

Margarito's Forest, Andy Carter (author), Allison Havens (illustrator), Omar Mejia (Translator)

Trailer Park – Jennifer Dillard (author), Madelin Arroyo (translator), Anna Usacheva (Illustrations)

Made in the USA
Middletown, DE
25 October 2020

22590821R00092